Home is Where I Belong

Eleanor A. Biletski

Home is Where I Belong
ISBN 0-9784111-0-2

Published by the Author

Original cover concept by the Author, based on a childhood sketch and an original family photograph. Realization by Vanessa Benson.

Book Design by John Breeze

Printed in Canada

To my sisters, Dora, Jean & Elaine
and in memory of
my mom, Helen Alice,
and
my daddy, Ignace John.

Acknowledgements

A very special "thank you" to all my family for your love and support.

I am also very grateful to my colleagues in IPAC, the Independent Publishers Association of Canada, for getting me back on track and for providing the incentive I needed to pursue my dream.

A heartfelt "thank you" to John Breeze for bringing this book to print. Thanks for your editing expertise, for your advice, and for pushing me forward to complete this project. I couldn't, and wouldn't, have done it without your help.

Eleanor

1

The clock on the dash displays twelve o'clock high noon as I approach "The Three-Mile Corner," which locals nicknamed the intersection east of home. I had traveled all night, my mind alert and active, savoring precious memories of the past. The arrow on the sign points in the direction of the small town where I spent my childhood. Calling it a town is an exaggeration. It is small, even for a village. I turn left onto the narrow graveled road flanked by flat fields dotted with clumps of shrubs and groves of trees. I had made the same trip several times over the years, but this visit would be different, because the building which I called home had been torn down, and the lot has been sold. Deep in thought, I pass the cemetery a mile down the road. I back up and pull into the driveway. Stopping here on my way home has become a ritual. I get out, push open the metal gate, and make my way through the dry stubble to my mother's grave. The sun feels hot overhead as I kneel down beside it. Mom chose to be buried here next to her first husband. Her second husband, my daddy, is buried in the cemetery on the other side of town. It occurs to me that I still call him "Daddy." Memories of my father fill my mind as I return to the car to complete the last two miles of my journey. I park in front of the Roman Catholic Church deciding to approach the site on foot.

It is Sunday, and Main Street is deserted. A gust of wind

drifting toward me down the street envelopes me in a cloud of dust as I walk. From a distance, our lot looks strangely empty but very much as I pictured it in my mind. It is engulfed in tall, dead grass. Stark new growth in the landfill clearly defines the area where the building rested for so many years. The two shacks are still standing. I am drawn to my favorite spot on the lot, taking small steps; steps taking me back to the old days, days when I visited the big rock. I hope it is still there, my rock. I sense I must be getting close to the spot, getting warmer and warmer. Instead of being greeted by the rock, I discover a large hollow in the earth. The rock appears to have been recently removed, evidence being the broken shrubs and grass, which are ripped away forming a path that I follow to the lane where it must have been hauled away.

Feeling tired, hot, and emotionally drained, I return to the spot where my rock once stood. As I kneel down and snuggle into the nest left by the body of the rock, I realize that this place will forever be my home even though the rock and the building in which I grew up are gone. I find coolness and comfort in the hollow and an overwhelming closeness to home as I lie there, assuming a fetal position, and close my eyes. My mind rewinds and stops, almost with a click.

Mentally, I push "Start." The memories begin with the first words I can remember, ironic words, which pump energy into my mind and body. "Go, Johnny! Go, Johnny, go!" cheers a familiar voice. I look over my shoulder and spot my sister standing in the distance. She is almost twelve years older than I am and has the power to do anything, even to change me from a girl into a boy. She tucked my brown hair under my cap and dressed me up in jeans and a shirt. It's so easy to be a boy. I ride my tricycle better than any boy can. I like being five years old, but I love my tricycle. I pedal down the path that runs along Main Street in front of our so-called store. The street itself is only a short graveled road lined with several stores and businesses, which include a post office and the hotel next door to our place.

When I spot a car turning onto the street, I spin my "trike" around and hurry back to my yard before the dust can reach me. I hate it. Imagine that we all turn into dust after we die. I whisper the words, "Ashes to ashes, and dust to dust." After parking the tricycle, I rip off my cap and run past the old shacks and outhouse to the large granite rock that juts out of the long grass in front of the clump of willow bushes and poplar trees near the back of our lot. The rock is over three feet high at one end and slopes down to less than a foot in height at the other. It is at least two and a half feet wide all the way down and resembles a compact slide, facing north. I climb on, sit down, and pull my knees up under my chin.

I had heard the story about my birthday numerous times. The day before I was born, there was a blizzard, which is not unusual for the middle of May in this part of the country. My mom was taken to the hospital town about twenty miles away by a jigger on the train tracks because the roads were blocked. People gathered at the station at the other end of Main Street to watch as she was loaded onto the open-air apparatus and bundled up with blankets. I was born the next day, a Sunday, which happened to be Mother's Day, bringing to mind a rhyme that ends with the words: "The child who's born on the Sabbath Day is bonnie and blithe, and good and gay!" My mother most certainly didn't agree, though it wasn't because I was born on the Sabbath Day. She already had three daughters and had prayed for a son. In many countries, it's a well-known fact that women are valued for the number of sons they produce.

Besides, Mom was forty-two years old and I would be her last child. Making matters worse was the fact that Big Sister, who was only nineteen years old, had just given birth to a son a week earlier and was still in the same hospital because he had respiratory problems. Mom didn't look at me for three days and cried the entire time, which pretty much snuffed out the bonding process. Finally, in a last ditch attempt, the nurses wrapped me up in a fancy blanket, brushed my dark hair into a curl on top of my head, and took me to her. She admitted later that I looked at her with my big eyes seeming to ask what I had done that was so wrong. It was fortunate for me, at least, on that particular day, that my mother was such a staunch Christian. She feared God might punish her for her actions and decided to accept me. I had two sisters; half-sisters, really, waiting for me at home. Medium Sister was was twelve years old, and Small Sister was six.

As I squirm around on the rock trying to get comfortable, I speak to myself as I often do. "Why didn't my mother trade babies with Big Sister?" I ask and am about to continue when I am interrupted.

"Perhaps she should have, because your sister will end up having four boys and no girls," answers a captivating male voice from out of the blue.

"Who are you?" I dare to ask. As a result of being startled and frightened, I begin to tremble.

"Don't be afraid. I'm here to guide you, something like a fairy godmother. It'll be our secret. I can be your big brother, and I'll be here for you at the big rock whenever you think you need someone to talk to."

"Why should you care about me? I'm just a little girl nobody else cares about," I confess trying not to fall under his spell, but I know deep down inside me that it is already too late. I am completely at his mercy.

"All I can say is that you are lucky to be a girl and that you are going to grow up in this end-of-the-line town. You'll learn a lot about life and yourself, and you'll come to appreciate the little things and question things you don't think are right." I leave the rock looking back over my shoulder to make sure he isn't following me. It occurs to me that he must refer to this place as the end of the line because the railroad tracks stop here. He seems to know so much about me. I must face the fact that I am no longer alone, which scares me yet, at the same time, comforts me.

2

Everyone thinks I'm spoiled because I have some dolls, a tricycle, and a daddy. My sisters never had any dolls or a tricycle, and their father is dead. My daddy is at work on the railroad way up north. I feel bewildered because I don't know what my daddy looks like. He has been gone for months, and my memory doesn't go back that far. He comes home only once in a while for a couple of weeks at a time. My sisters' father also worked on the railroad. One day, his employer's officials notified Mom that he had yellow fever. She immediately traveled by train to the hospital out east to be with him. Little did she know that while he was at work he had actually slipped on ice and fallen on the job while carrying a heavy crate of supplies, hitting his head on a doorsill—the truth as revealed to her later by his co-workers. He was conscious when she arrived and recognized her, but could not speak. He communicated with her by writing on a notepad, but had difficulty manipulating his fingers, and his condition gradually worsened. Mom had decided to leave her daughters at home with the oldest in charge. Big Sister was only fifteen, and her younger sisters were only eight and two years old at the time. The accident happened in the middle of winter. Mom was away for a longer period of time than anyone could have expected, spending all of two months with him. My sisters were running out of food, and there was no firewood left by the time my mom returned on the train. She told them she had brought their father home. They ran to the door to greet him but met men carrying in his coffin, instead. Mom was never the same after he died. She received no compensation, and it's unsettling to me that my daddy is working for the same railroad.

Shortly after the funeral, relatives informed my mother that they knew of a man, my soon-to-be daddy, who was interested in marriage. Mom was vulnerable. She was a widow with three young daughters. Arrangements were made by letter. He traveled a great distance to meet her, made her his wife, bundled up the girls, and moved them to his place out east. Teachers failed to convince Big Sister to stay behind and finish high school. She chose to leave with the rest of the family. Two years later, at the age of seventeen, she married the boy from across the back lane. The whole family moved back to the end of the line to run the hardware store.

Big Sister and her new husband had the upstairs of the building to themselves. It consisted of two huge rooms with a rectangular-shaped attic running along the east side of the room facing Main Street—although we called it "the attic", it was really no more than a cubbyhole. The store was located on the ground floor, under their two rooms. Beneath the attic itself were three rooms, with another small one at the back entrance separated from the others by a curtain. The room closest to Main Street was a bedroom furnished with a double bed, a dresser, and a desk. A door on the south wall opened onto the street. The middle room was the living room decorated with a burgundy plush sofa, two armchairs, and a couple of small tables. The third room was the kitchen, which contained a wood-burning cookstove, some cupboards along the short wall, a wooden table with several chairs, and a bench on which stood a pail of drinking water.

A door in the floor of the back room opened into a root cellar that was usually full of water. We had to keep our food cool in the cellar because there was no electricity to power a refrigerator; coal oil lamps, gas lanterns, and candles provided our lighting. In the store were counters, running lengthwise along both sides of the spacious main room. Floor-to-ceiling shelves lined the walls behind the counters. A display table, approximately ten feet by six feet in size, took up the middle of the room. At the back of the room stood a wood-burning heater which, along with the kitchen cookstove, heated the lower floor of the building. Two posts supported the high ceiling. One was located approximately eight feet from the front door that opened onto Main Street from a porch-like entrance; the other was near the back of the store. In front of the rear post rested my favorite piece of furniture—a heavy wooden loveseat with a padded leather seat cover. Its curved back and arms were beautifully carved with a cutout grapevine pattern.

Clothing, papers, and other paraphernalia littered the living quarters; dishes were never all washed and put away at any one particular time. My mother was not an organized housekeeper. Although she was a good cook, we never seemed to sit down for a meal together. She could sew beautifully, even without a pattern. Her treadle sewing machine was proudly displayed in the living room next to the sofa. Most of her time, be it spring, summer, or fall, was spent preparing for winter, which dictated our lives. Every one of us struggled to meet its challenge for survival.

Mom was born on the family homestead eight miles away. When she finished Grade IV, she was forced to quit school to work on her parents' farm. There were stones to pick in the fields, cows to milk, and weeds to pull in their huge garden. She never had shoes to wear and described her doll as being a corncob wrapped in a piece of cloth.

Big Sister's son and I were treated like twins when we were babies. I was the aggressive one, always pushing him away and wanting attention. Shortly after our first birthday, Big Sister, her husband, and their little boy moved back to the town out east. They had lost too much money on the store, and he had a job waiting for him there. They left behind their black Cocker Spaniel, Smoky, who was two years old. Besides Smoky, all that remained to remind me of them was the delicate rose-flowered and blue-ribboned paper on the walls upstairs.

3

I'm so lucky to be spoiled, and I'm especially lucky today because my daddy is coming home. I will soon see him for the first time—I mean, for the first time I can remember. All of a sudden, I hear him coming in the back door so I run and hide. Then I peek around the doorway between the living room and kitchen. After catching a glimpse of me, he sets down some parcels and his suitcases and stretches his arms out in my direction as he calls my name. I run to him, and he scoops me up and whirls me around. I feel the stubble on his cheek as he gives me a hug. Now I see who looks like me. His hair is the same color as mine, not blonde like my sisters'. The shape of my face, nose, and mouth are like his and our eyes are the same shade of blue. My sisters, according to my mother, favor their own father.

My daddy is not a tall man, but he seems ten feet tall to me today. He has presents for us—a blue cotton dress for Small Sister and one for me, too. Mine has a Peter Pan collar and a white eyelet yoke with a lace-fringed ruffle around it. I run to the bedroom and slip it on. Daddy smiles approvingly when I return to the kitchen and ties the wide strands attached at the sides to form a big bow in the back above the skirt that is gathered at the waist. I love it, but I love the shoes he also brought me more. They are made of chartreuse leather with a perforated flower pattern on the vamp, a T-strap, and a silver buckle on the side. I practice opening and closing the buckles. Then I head for the path in front of the store. Daddy chuckles as I walk along and stop every few steps to wipe the dust off my special shoes to make them shine again. When I return to the kitchen, he is preparing to have a shave at the basin next to the water bucket. His train trip home lasted more than a day, resulting in the thick growth on his face. The air is permeated with a sweet, spicy fragrance when he opens his suitcase. I close my eyes for a moment in order to concentrate fully on my sense of smell. Then I open them and watch with interest as he removes his razor, shaving cream, and lotion. I notice that he also keeps his clock, a deck of cards, and some papers in the suitcase. As he lathers his face in front of the mirror above the wash stand, he quickly reaches out and flicks some shaving cream on my nose.

My daddy is a jolly person, who is always laughing and joking around. He has plenty of pet names for me. Most of the Ukrainian ones mean either "little belly button" or "little pile of poop." Others constantly tease me about the names, but I don't care. My favorite pet name is "caboose" which, of course, isn't Ukrainian. Daddy can read and write in his native language and learned how to read English by poring over our daily newspaper through his reading glasses. He explains to me that many letters in the Ukrainian and English alphabets look and sound the same. In Ukrainian, every letter of a word is sounded. Daddy often uses the same method in his pronunciation of words in English. When a little green bug lands on my arm, he, obviously, thinks about how the word is printed in English and comes up with, "Lit-lee, green bug. Let live," with a long "i" as in "alive."

I often crawl up on his knee and beg him to draw for me. The picture he draws is always the same, a sketch of an old man. He draws a side view beginning with the cap and peak, then the forehead, long nose, protruding chin, and stringy hair flowing from under the cap. The man's coat has a collar and three buttons. He has skinny legs; his shoes have heels and his arm extends in front of him with his hand holding a cane. The finishing touches consist of a beady eye, bushy eyebrow, curvy ear, and a pipe sticking out of the man's mouth. He always waits for me to ask him to draw smoke coming out of the pipe. I never want the drawing to end. Daddy also teaches me to play cards—Solitaire; "Holla," which is a Ukrainian game meaning "naked;" and my favorite, Poker, that included many different games.

No matter what we do, time spent with Daddy passes all too quickly. The day before his departure is filled with anguish for me. I run out the back door, stand on the step, and call, "Smoky, here, Smoky!" Within seconds, the dog appears with his stubby tail wagging excitedly. I cup my hands over his curly ears and pull his face close to mine. Tears come to my eyes as I peer into his sad ones and whisper, "Daddy is leaving tomorrow. Come with me." I run down the path and climb onto my rock. "Big Brother, are you there?" I call.

"Of course, I'm here. And I know why you are sad."

"I wish my daddy could stay with me forever. I don't want him to go."

"Well, Little Johnny, you better get used to it because your life is going to be full of good-byes and you will have to be responsible for yourself most of the time. You must be thankful for the little time you do spend with your daddy. You hate to say good-bye but think about how happy you will be when you see him again." I stare straight ahead barely seeing the log barn and the grove of trees behind it through my tears.

Tomorrow comes. "Bye, my daddy," I manage to say as I hug him tightly around his neck. He gently sets me down and picks up his duffel bag and little black suitcase. He starts down the path and then turns until our eyes meet. I wave, just a little wave. Then I force my mouth into smile so that my Daddy will never guess how upset I am and watch him until he disappears around the corner.

4

Shortly after Big Sister and her family left, Mom moved our sleeping quarters upstairs. There are a couple of beds in the front room—a double bed under the Main Street windows and a single bed across the room from the opening to the attic. In the back room, next to Mom's double bed, stands a box stove. It is a heating apparatus constructed of tin with a lid on top that can be flipped open when loading wood and a damper at the bottom front. Black pipes lead from the back of the stove to an elbow close to the ceiling and then outside through the wall. The window beside her bed faces north, and the door next to it opens onto a wooden balcony and fire exit. Wood for stoking the stove is carried up the fire escape stairs. I have my choice of sleeping spots. Sometimes I sleep at the foot of the bed with my sisters, in the single bed across from the attic opening, or with my mother when Daddy isn't home. On cold nights, Mom builds a fire in the box stove. The tin turns a glowing red from the extreme heat and shadows are cast on the walls from the firelight shining through the damper.

I name the front bedroom downstairs "the Main Street Bedroom." Big Sister slept in that room when she was in her teens. She recalled waking up one night and seeing our grandmother's body surrounded by candles and mourners crying silently. Her father's coffin was also kept in that room before his funeral. She remembered relatives examining his skull and seeing evidence of his injury herself. Without a doubt, he did not die from yellow fever as claimed by the company. A hodgepodge of people stayed in the Main Street Bedroom over the years. My mother charged some of them rent and took others in because they had nowhere else to go. She told us stories about a nurse and her husband who lived in the room for more that a year. It had also been a nursery for an infant placed in my mother's care for several months before I was born

One day, I overhear a conversation between my mother and one of her many visitors who often drop in unannounced. Mom informs her that the priest from her church and his wife will be staying in the Main Street Bedroom for six weeks and teaching the Ukrainian language and Ukrainian dancing when regular school is out for the summer. I am somewhat excited, yet frightened, of the prospect of having holy people staying at our house. I wonder what they will look like, these holy people. Perhaps they will have halos around their heads like Jesus does in the pictures hanging on our living room wall. Will his voice sound like thunder just like God's? What will my mother feed these special people?

On the day of the arrival of the priest and his wife, I look forward to having my questions answered. I am playing outside with Smoky when they come in the front door. Mom has moved a table into the rear area of the store so that there would be enough room to accommodate everyone at mealtime. I sneak in unnoticed and quickly survey the people around the table. I guess that the man in the black suit is the priest, but something is missing. He has no halo and neither does his wife. They both look strangely ordinary. He is a pudgy man with fat fingers crossed on his round belly. A fringe of dark hair surrounds his head, and the closest thing to a halo is the light that glances off the top of his bald spot from the flickering gas lantern that hangs from the ceiling. His wife is wearing a dark dress cut fairly low in the front revealing some cleavage. Her shoulder-length dark hair is parted in the middle and clipped back behind her ears with little combs. They are both wearing shiny black leather shoes. I closely peruse her heavy legs, which are covered with lightweight beige stockings. His voice is much higher than I expected and not at all like thunder. I listen to them chat for a while and soon become bored because most of the conversation is in Ukrainian. I creep upstairs after scrounging a sandwich and crawl into bed utterly disappointed with the appearance of the holy couple.

On Sunday, the priest will hold a sermon at the church. Mom informs me that I will be attending the service with her. I am up early in the morning feeling nervous because it will be my first time. Mom and I wear dresses. Before we leave the house, she ties a flowered kerchief on her head and orders me to wear one too. I hate it because I think it makes me look ugly. God supposedly gave me my hair so why should I have to cover it up?

We walk to church in silence with each of us absorbed in our own thoughts. The gate to the churchyard is open. I follow my mother up the cement steps. She hesitates a moment before she opens the door. Once inside, Mom kneels on the floor, crosses herself, begins to pray, and motions for me to do the same. After pretending to pray, I sit beside her in the last pew. A red carpet leads to the altar that has a gold book on it. The walls on both sides of the altar are decorated with holy pictures. Another one on the front of the altar is of a little girl with her hands held in prayer and her eyes looking upward. She wears a white dress. A lock of her blonde hair is held in place on the top of her head with a large white bow. Most of the pictures are of men with long hair and wearing dresses. I recognize those of Virgin Mary from the pictures of her hanging in our living room. The room behind the altar is adorned with a large arch featuring double doors that join in the middle. The doors are decorated with cutout carvings of clusters of grapes and vines. Behind the doors, a burgundy satin curtain hangs on golden rings. Both sides of the fancy doors are flanked with open narrow arched doorways leading to the room behind the curtain.

Women and children sit in the pews on the left. Men sit on the right. They don't wear anything on their heads even though most of them are bald. The priest pulls the curtain aside and opens the double doors to signal the beginning of the service. Everyone stands up at once as he begins to sing in Ukrainian in his rather whiny, high voice. He is wearing a very expensive-looking long greenish cape with an all-over shiny gold design. He alternates between singing and speaking, and one of the bald men makes responses in a loud booming voice. Every so often, two other men carry lit candles in wooden pillars, approximately three feet high, through the doorways but always return to stand in front of the altar. The priest then swings a small golden container on a chain with a fancy jerking motion causing strong-smelling smoke to drift out over the people as they bow their heads. The service seems to last forever. The only word I understand is "Amen," but he pronounces it "Aw mean." He repeats it over and over again so I know he is doing plenty of praying. Then a plate is passed around, and I place my coin in it noticing a lot of the money collected from the men's side of the room. I spend most of my time watching a fly that crawls on the window and then flies onto the hat of a woman sitting in front of us. It crawls repeatedly, in time to the singing, from her hat to her shoulders and back to her hat again. Finally a hush fills the church. Everyone forms a line and takes their turn kissing a gold cross with Jesus nailed to it. After the old men kiss it, I don't find kissing it too appealing so, when my turn comes, I just pretend to kiss it. Then we each get a piece of bread that doesn't taste like ordinary bread and is of a thicker texture. It is very good and makes attending church worth my while. Mom and I discuss the service as we walk home. "Are girls allowed to enter the room behind the altar?" I ask because I hope to see what is behind that curtain one day.

"Women are only allowed in there to dust and clean," she admits.

"I don't think that's fair, "I reply.

Smoky is waiting for me on the front step and barks at me because he doesn't like my kerchief either. I am happy to see he agrees with me so I slip it off and hand it to my mother. I run to the big rock with my dog at my heels. "Big Brother, are you there? I went to church today, and something is really bothering me."

"Johnny, Little Johnny. Yes, I'm here."

"I don't think God likes girls very much."

"What makes you say that?"

"Well, girls must wear something on their head in church and boys don't have to. The men are allowed to hold candles and walk around in the room behind the curtain. All women can do is clean up the mess in there. Boys can sing to the priest like they are in a play but girls can't, and I don't think girls can be priests."

"You are right about all of these things. In time, however, girls will be able to do everything that boys can do in the church. It won't be because the church regards females as being equal to males. It will happen because males will lose interest in the church, and the church will need females to fill their positions."

"I don't think I'd want to be a priest anyway. I've got to go. I'll be talking to you."

5

School is out for the summer. More than anything, my sisters want to sleep in, but Mom drags them out of bed for the Ukrainian language classes held at the school. They are also required to attend dancing classes at the hall beside Mom's church. Their dance troupe's goal is to perform in the big town to celebrate the end of Ukrainian summer school. Both of my sisters receive a costume that consists of a knee-length red skirt decorated with row upon row of ribbon sewn above the hem line, a white blouse with billowing sleeves adorned with red and black embroidery, and a black velveteen vest. The headdress is a garland of flowers with long ribbons attached to it. They look beautiful when they dance in their group with their skirts, sleeves, and ribbons swirling as they move in time to the music.

I also attend dance practice because I am to take part in the grand finale of the concert. Mom makes my elf costume. On my head I will wear antennae constructed of wires covered with lime-green crepe paper attached to a headband. My lime-green pants billow out on the legs and are held in place with elastic at the ankles. The matching lime-green cotton shoes have their toes curled up with the help of thin wires. A brown cardigan sweater with a beige and white pattern on the front completes the outfit. Later, I also receive a dance costume similar to my sisters'.

The day of the concert finally arrives. I am so excited because we are to be treated to a ride in the priest's car.

The trip ends up being long and dull, because I am sandwiched between two big people in the back seat and can't even see out the windows. The hall is spacious with a high ceiling, a stage at one end, and rows of chairs for the audience. I play with a little girl, who I think is very pretty. For some reason, the way she acts and speaks gives me the impression that she comes from a rich family. She is wearing a white dress with a huge matching bow tied to a lock of her blonde hair on top of her head. She reminds me of the girl in the picture at Mom's church and also of a girl whose picture was on a letter that Mom received in the mail. That girl was wearing a brace on her leg. I saw Mom put money in the envelope, which was sent to the Easter Seal Campaign; I think she should have used the money to buy us food because we never had enough to eat. Anyway, that girl was also wearing a white dress and a white bow in her blonde hair and was probably rich, too. Before the concert gets under way, everyone taking part in it gathers on the stage for the photographer. I am ordered to kneel in the front row in the center beside the pretty girl and just ahead of the priest and his wife. After pictures are taken, the stage is cleared. The lights above the audience go out, spotlights are directed onto the stage, and a hush fills the room.

Various groups perform. I enjoy the sight of all the colorful costumes, the singing, and the Ukrainian music that always makes my heart beat faster and fills me with so much emotion it brings tears to my eyes. I can barely sit still. Then it is time for my dance, the last item on the program. I wait impatiently behind the curtain while my group acts out the first part of the routine. When the girls and boys form a long line, the priest's wife whispers, "Hurry, hurry! On to the stage with you," in Ukrainian. The couples face each other arranged in height from tallest to shortest. With their arms crossed in front of them, they hold each other's hands forming a bridge several feet above the floor. As the tempo of the music increases, two boys hoist me up; and I carefully walk along the bridge of arms placing one foot in front of the other on their wrists. The audience begins to clap in time to the music. Then the lights blind my eyes. I glance down to get my bearings and watch, in disbelief, as the curled-up toe of my lime-green shoe disappears through the bridge as the hands of the couple in the middle lose their grip. The people in the audience gasp in unison as I begin to fall. Just in the nick of time, I manage to pull myself up with the help of two dancers who come to my rescue. I steady myself while I hold onto their hands, make my way to the end of the bridge, hop down, and bow. The audience loves the ending. Applause and cheering abound as the curtain closes, and everyone fusses over me backstage. I am pleased with my performance and hum the finale music as I sit on a chair in the corner while the dancers remove their costumes.

I wake up in bed the next morning not knowing how I got home. I hate Sundays. It seems that everyone goes to the except us, because we don't own a car. Buying one would be pointless because Daddy is never at home to drive us around anyway. Smoky and I sit on the front step watching cars speed by headed in the direction of the beach. Finally, the dust they raise forces us to head for the big rock. I perch myself on the very tip. "Well, Johnny, how was the concert?" asks Big Brother taking my mind off not being able to go to the lake.

"It was fun, and I was the star. I almost slipped through the bridge of arms, but all the practicing I did swinging between the counter and the shelves in the store must have made my arms so strong I kept myself from falling. I met a pretty girl wearing a white dress and a big bow in her blonde hair at the concert. I wonder if I will ever be pretty."

"I can see you entering a café on a cold winter's night.

You are hurrying through the outside door into the lobby and are about to open the main door when a voice calls, 'Hi, Beautiful.' You turn around thinking the compliment surely couldn't be meant for you. A young man with a sunny smile is following you into the cafe. You whisper, 'Hi!,' because you can see that he does mean 'you.' Now, in another instance, I can see you sitting in a cafe in the big town. You are traveling somewhere and waiting for a train. A handsome young fellow walks over and joins you at your table. You are almost finished your lunch so he orders two more soft drinks just to keep you around. Then he stands up and saunters over to the jukebox. He looks back at you, grins, and makes a selection."

Catching me off guard, Johnny begins to sing, "Pretty woman, walking down the street, pretty woman the kind you like to meet. Pretty woman..."

"So you're sure it will happen one day. I love your song and I love your voice," I reply as I leave the rock with a joyous feeling in my heart, humming the song, and hoping I will start getting beautiful and pretty as soon as possible.

6

Frizzy and her brother come to visit later that day. Frizzy is a short, stout woman who lives with her husband just down the street and around the corner. They own a barbershop, sell ice cream and milkshakes, and run the town telephone switchboard. I call her "Frizzy" because she has black permed hair. She speaks in a shrill voice but can always make me laugh. Her brother is vacationing from out west. He sits on the loveseat and pats the space beside him for me to come and join him. Then he gently lifts me up and sets me on his knee, and I notice that he smells familiar. Yes, without a doubt, he uses the same shaving lotion as my daddy. He gives me a quarter for popcorn and promises that he will see me again before his vacation is over. True to his word, they do visit often.

Late one night, shortly after Frizzy's brother left, a severe storm rumbles in without warning. Mom wakes us up and orders us downstairs. She is terrified of thunder and lightning and makes us put on our jackets and rubber boots in case the house is hit. Rain is beating on the roof, and the wind is howling. Mom lights a candle that has been blessed at her church, believing that it has the power to keep us safe from the storm. We sit on the edge of the sofa waiting for lighting to strike but are startled by loud banging at the kitchen door instead. When lightning flashes, we see Frizzy's terrified face in the window. Mom lets her in, struggling to close the door against the force of the wind, and turns the skeleton key in the lock. Frizzy, soaking wet and shivering, is carrying a suitcase. Mom instinctively blows out the candle, and the room returns to complete darkness. Through chattering teeth, Frizzy informs us that she has had a big fight with her husband and that he is chasing her with a butcher knife. Suddenly, he is at the window with a flashlight peering in. We crouch down behind the entrance to the kitchen and gasp when we see the knife blade flash as lightning strikes again. He pounds on the door swearing for only minutes, but it seems like an eternity. Then he gives up and slithers away. He couldn't know for certain that Frizzy escaped to our place. Frizzy and Mom must have stayed awake for the remainder of the night. I fall asleep propped up in the corner of the sofa without removing my boots or jacket.

In the morning, I awaken to see Frizzy unpacking her suitcase and transferring the contents into two cardboard boxes. She offers me the suitcase, because she has decided to leave her husband to make a new life for herself out west and no longer wants it because it would be a constant reminder of him. It is a large brown suitcase with gold metal snaps. Under the circumstances, I don't know if I should thank her for it but must admit, at least to myself, that I really like it.

Frizzy catches a ride out of town with the taxi. Since I am still dressed in my jacket and boots, I decide to head for the rock. The morning air is cool even though the sun is shining brightly, and the rain barrel at the side of the house is overflowing. As I round the corner, I see Mom standing by the garden. "Look at the rainbow," she says. My eyes follow the direction of her pointing finger. The half-circle of bright colors is the most beautiful thing I have ever seen. In amazement, I draw in a quick breath. "The rainbow is God's promise that there will be no more rain for three days," explains my mom.

"And there is supposed to be a pot of gold at the end of the rainbow, but nobody has ever found it," hollers Medium Sister from inside the house as I continue on my way. Droplets of water trickle onto my head and shoulders from the leaves overhead. Branches litter the yard, and the wind and rain have beaten down the tall grass around the buildings. The moisture-laden rock glistens in the sun.

"Good morning, Big Brother," I call. "Frizzy's husband really scared me last night. I wish married people wouldn't fight. They should talk and laugh and go for long walks together holding hands and enjoying each other's company."

"Good morning to you, Little Sister. I agree, but most

marriages don't often turn out that way. Perhaps, it's because males and females are too different."

"Frizzy gave me a beautiful suitcase to keep for my very own. I put it under Mom's bed upstairs. If her husband ever sees it, he will know that we were hiding her. I don't think I will ever see Frizzy again."

"That suitcase will be very special and useful to you because you will move around a lot. I see it filled with clothes and books that change with the years. I can see a white satin gown, a bouquet of white satin rosebuds intertwined with lily-of-the-valley, and a pair of white leather slippers with fluffy trim on the vamps in it. These items will be stored in the suitcase for a long time." Big Brother always gives me something interesting to think about. Thoughts of the gown and bouquet fill my mind as I walk away from the rock. To my disappointment, the rainbow has already disappeared from the morning sky.

7

Our home seems to attract people like a magnet. Some are visitors, some come to eat, and some live with us for a while. Some are strange and some are special. Old Man Click is one of the strange ones. On the evening of our first encounter, he comes over from the hotel smelling of stale beer and cigars and is obviously drunk. I am somewhat afraid of him and watch from a safe distance as Mom serves him coffee, soup, and a canned meat sandwich. I name him "Old Man Click" because his cane goes, "Click, click, click," on the wooden floor in the store. Whenever I hear the noise of that cane, I know Old Man Click is around and make myself scarce. He is always happy to see my father, and they are great friends. Sometimes his hands shake so badly that Daddy has to feed him his soup with a big spoon. The more beer he drinks at the hotel, the more his hands shake. When he finishes eating, they have a grand time singing dirty Ukrainian songs, which I don't really understand.

Because he is very thin, Old Man Click looks tall, but is only the same height as my dad. The skin on his narrow face is wrinkled with age. He sports a stringy gray mustache and watery blue eyes. Taking his features into consideration, I decide he is definitely the man in the pictures my daddy sketches for me. Most of the time he wears a pair of fur-lined pants constructed of patches of tan shiny leather that are randomly sewn together. He proudly states, "I was born in these pants, married in these pants, and will die in these pants." He moved into town from the farm that he could no longer manage after his wife died. He constantly boasts that he is ready to die, too. It is a true statement, according to my dad, who claims that Old Man Click has a coffin, which he built for himself in his house across the tracks, and that he stores his money in it.

Late in the fall, a special old woman comes to spend the winter with us. Her husband passed away, but she continued to live in the country with her cats for some time. She would not keep a fire in her stove at night for fear of burning down her house. Her cats were known to sit on top of the stove in order to keep warm from the small fire she did allow to burn in the stove during the day. Neighbors were afraid she would freeze to death and convinced her to stay at our place. One chilly afternoon, she appears at our door with her suitcases and boxes. She is a very tall, fairly heavy-set woman dressed in a long black coat. On her head is perched a strangely-shaped bonnet moulded out of tightly-woven shiny black braiding. Its brim curls away from her forehead and is held in place with two black ribbons tied in a bow under her chin. Her round trifocals make her gray eyes appear enormous. She walks stooped over from the waist and keeps herself upright with her cane that makes delicate tapping noises, quite different from those of Old Man Click's cane. We carry her belongings into the Main Street Bedroom.

When she comes out for supper, she is wearing a long-sleeved black dress with buttons all the way down the front. The skirt falls almost to the floor, but when she bends over I can still see her black leather shoes with thick heels and laces up the front . She isn't using her cane and moves surprisingly well without it. Her silver hair is pulled back from her white face and twisted into a bun at the nape of her neck.

The table with the food is at the back of the store, where it was moved when the priest and his wife stayed with us. We all sit down to eat at the same time, which is a rare occurrence in our house. We begin helping ourselves but stop immediately when the old woman begins to pray out loud. After glancing at each other in surprise, we bow our heads and wait until she is finished. When she starts passing dishes around, we follow suit and join in. While she eats, she tells us stories about her life as a young girl, her years in the country, her love for her cats she regrettably had to leave with a neighbor, and her relationship with her husband. She asks that tea and a snack be served before going to bed. When the time comes, we are anxiously sitting around the table waiting for her. Finally, she appears and sits down with us as we bow our heads in anticipation of grace. To our surprise, she begins helping herself to toast and tea. We watch her curiously. When she realizes that we were waiting for her to pray, she smiles and announces that she recites grace only before supper. After we finish eating, we sit around until midnight listening to more of her stories.

One night, after she has been with us for about a week, she notices my watching her as she prepares herself for bed. With a wave of her hand, she invites me to enter her room. She has removed her dress, leaving her wearing only an undershirt and a kind of corset. My mouth drops open, and I can't help but stare at the outline of her pendulous breasts underneath the shirt. After struggling out of her corset, she stands there in a pair of dusty pink fleece bloomers. She tosses the laced undergarment on a chair and sits down on the edge of the bed in order to slip off her brown cotton stockings. My attention focuses on her legs, which are wrapped in strips of cloth, resembling those of a mummy. Then she unravels the long strips from both legs. The skin on her legs is transparent allowing the blue veins to shine through it. She rubs a substance that looks like lard on her legs taking time to massage it into her skin, slips on a nightgown, and lets down her hair that falls to her waist. With experienced fingers, she quickly forms it into a braid.

She orders me to fetch the newspaper, which is delivered daily. When I return, she is already in bed so I hand her the paper. She proceeds to take out the comics and flips over one end of the feather tick. I instinctively crawl in beside her. As she drapes her arm around me, I snuggle close to her. She is nice and warm and smells like ointment. She reads me the likes of "O' Henry," "Little Lulu," "Dagwood," "Dick Tracy," "Rex Morgan MD," and "Mary Worth." I don't care for the last three very much but decide not to complain because I want her to keep on reading. By the time she reads about Mary Worth, I summon up enough courage to ask her about the letters in the words. She points to the "M" and sounds, "Mmm, as in 'me,'" and then to "a," "ah, as in 'apple,'" and so on. After listening to her read the comics every day, I learn the alphabet; and I am aware of the fact that I can read some words and guess at others with amazing accuracy. The old woman, whom I quickly embrace as my teacher, knows that my grandmother died before I was born. One evening, after my comics lesson, she asks, "Would you like to call me 'Granny'?"

"That would make me so happy, Granny!" I respond before she has a chance to change her mind. Her favorite possessions are a globe of the world and a book with a black cover, which she claims is very important to her at this crucial period of time in her life. The book bears the title, "The Holy Bible," inscribed in gold letters on its hard leather cover. She admits that the older she becomes the more her interest in religion grows. Her time on earth is running out, compelling her to come to a decision as to whether or not there is a heaven and, God forbid, a hell and in which of those places she might end up. She offers to teach me about the Bible because every little girl growing up in a Christian community should know something about the sacred book.

My first lesson, which focuses on the Old Testament and its first book, Genesis, describes how the earth and the heavens were created. Granny regurgitates what she interprets from her readings combined with what she learned over the years in her own words saying, "God supposedly rested on the seventh day of the week after the creation. Christians believe that the week begins on a Monday so their day of rest is Sunday, the Sabbath. The Sabbath for the Jews lasts from Friday evening to Saturday evening. I reckon that much of the information presented in the stories of the Bible does not make sense. For instance, in Genesis 2:15-18, God warns Adam that if he ate fruit from the tree of knowledge he would surely die—which didn't happen. Adam ate the fruit blaming Eve for inciting him to eat it but was only kicked out of the Garden of Eden. In Genesis 3:24, God placed a flaming sword, which flashed back and forth, at the east side of the garden to keep Adam out; but I can't understand why God would own a sword in the first place. Eve gave birth to two sons, Cain and Abel, and I quote from Genesis 4:16-18, 'the Lord put a mark on Cain so that no-one who found him would kill him', and he 'went out from the Lord's presence and lived in the land of Nod, east of Eden. Cain lay with his wife, and she became pregnant and gave birth to Enoch. Cain was then building a city, and named it after his son Enoch.'" Granny pauses and asks, "If God created Adam and Eve as the first and only people on earth, where in the world did the people of Nod come from and enough of them to warrant building a city? Also, the God of the first part of the Bible, the Torah or Old Testament, was not a loving and forgiving God; but one who destroyed entire cities and, finally, all of the people of the world with the flood sparing only Noah and his family. Too bad God couldn't forgive Adam and Eve or the people in the cities, which he destroyed. Christianity expects us to forgive everyone for everything. That God was a vengeful God, a 'War Teacher,' who was often driven by wrath to plague people with pests, famine, and disease including leprosy. The Torah is chock-full of horrific stories about people who lied, stole, cheated, and committed murder and acts of incest without a shred of remorse. On the whole, they were a shabby lot," she concludes. I enjoy the lesson so much and wonder if school will be like this.

Now I spend the better part of my days scouring the house for books for Granny to read to me. One afternoon, I find an old Grade IV reader—a thick book with a hard cover and colored pictures, which usually form the borders for the print on its pages. That evening, I snuggle close to Granny in my usual spot as she flips through the pages of the reader with her long fingers until she comes to a story that seems familiar to her and stops turning the pages. She clears her throat noisily and announces the title of the story, "The Three Billy Goats Gruff." I see the picture of Big Billy Goat, Medium Billy Goat, and Small Billy Goat Gruff and imagine them to be my sisters, "Big Sis," "Med Sis," and "Small Sis." I'm not with them because my job is to watch and listen. I know they are crossing the bridge but can barely hear Granny's voice because all of my attention is focused on the picture of an ugly troll crouched under a bridge at the bottom of the page. His green transparent skin appears to be stretched tightly over his entire body, and blue veins shine through it. His hair is long, dark, and stringy, framing a face with bulging eyes, bushy eyebrows, and a long nose that dips down at the end and almost touches his large protruding lips. Green pointed ears stick out of his wispy hair.   Everything about him seems wicked, but his red eyes are especially evil. He sits under the bridge with his bony knees tucked under his chin and his gnarled hands clasped around them. He doesn't appear to be wearing anything except for a dark loincloth. I am so disturbed by the picture that I miss most of the story except for the ending, which I hear Granny read, "The Big Billy Goat Gruff bucks the troll off the bridge, and they cross over to the other side. The troll runs away and is never to be seen again, and that's the end of the story."

I whisper, "Good night, Granny. Thanks for reading to me." Then I run upstairs and crawl into bed without saying my prayers. I huddle close to my mother's back drawing some comfort from the warmth of her body; but the picture of the troll remains with me, even when I close my eyes. Hours pass before I fall into a fitful sleep.

8

One early November afternoon, I happen to be playing outdoors when I notice white flakes floating slowly and sparsely to the ground. I run into the kitchen calling, "Daddy, Daddy, it's snowing." He grabs my hand as we hurry out the back door together. I open my mouth and run around trying to catch the flakes on my tongue. I am so excited. "We'll be able to build snowmen, and Santa Claus will come soon. I can write him a letter and ask for anything I want. If I'm good, I'll get it." My daddy laughs, picks me up, and carries me back with snowflakes falling all around us.

It snows, and snows, and snows some more. Daddy is gone again. In the back yard, paths leading to the shacks, outhouse, and slop-heap develop in the deep snow. Night after night, Small Sis manages to convince me to accompany her to the toilet. We dress up in our jackets and boots and trudge out into the darkness trying not to slip off the path or we'd end up with a bootful of snow. Once inside, we pull down our fleece-lined bloomers and each take a seat. I always get the little hole. On moonlit nights, we leave the door open and play one of my favorite games. She is at the giggly stage when everything is so funny. The game is called "Grandfather's Big Fat Toe." She begins with the question, "Who is your boyfriend"? I must answer,

"Grandfather's Big Fat Toe," and not be allowed to laugh. I try my hardest to remain serious; but after a few more questions like, what is the best smell in the world? what did you eat for breakfast? and, what kind of toilet paper do you use? we both end up howling with laughter that echoes into the darkness. Toilet paper is a treat. Usually, we tear a couple of pages out of the old catalogue, crumple them up, and rub the paper back and forth in the palms of our hands until they are soft enough for use. Sometimes, we even use tissue, which was, at one time, wrapped around pears or apples to protect them from bruising when being shipped. When we get up to leave, our bums are always at least partially frozen.

A sure sign that Christmas is on its way is the appearance of two holiday catalogues that arrive by mail within a few days of each other. Most of our clothes, fabric, and household goods are ordered C.O.D. (cash on delivery), by filling out the name of the article, page number, color, size, and item number on a form accompanying each catalogue. The order is sent out by mail and the parcel is delivered by truck to the post office where we pay for it at the wicket. After the brown paper is torn off the catalogues, they make their rounds with my mother and sisters. I wait patiently for my turn and breathe a sigh of relief when I get them. Almost half of the pages are covered with shiny colored pictures of toys. After hours spent studying the different toys, I find the one I will ask for in my letter to Santa Claus. I carry the catalogue to Granny's room and knock gently on the arched doorway. She calls for me to enter. She is sitting at the desk in front of the window facing Main Street. The sun shines through the frosty design on the window and glances off the thick lenses of her spectacles to form a "straight rainbow" on her writing paper. In her hand, she holds a fountain pen, which she has just dipped into a bottle of blue ink on the right corner of the desk. She immediately clears a spot on the desk for the catalogue and begins to turn its pages. I stop her when she comes to the right one, point to a picture, and whisper, "Please read what it says about my Santa toy."

She begins to read, "Pumpkinhead, Santa's favorite little helper. Made of foam rubber, 12 inches high with a topknot on its head and a tail. Jacket, pants, eyes and nose painted on its brown body. Cost $2.98." She adds, "It looks like it has a teddy bear's eyes and nose, but it really is not a teddy bear."

"Is it a long time until Christmas?" I ask.

She checks her calendar with a picture of three kittens playing with a ball of red wool in a wicker basket on it, carefully counts the days, and comes up with the answer: "Thirty-seven days till Christmas."

"Please, can you, help me write a letter to Santa?" I ask. She pulls out a clean sheet of paper and dips the pen again. Then she hoists me onto her lap and guides my hand with the pen in it to help me form the blue letters that read: "Dear Santa, I have been a good girl and I would like a Pumpkinhead for Christmas." On the envelope we print: "Santa Claus, North Pole."

"Thank you, Granny," I murmur as I slide off her lap and leave her room with the catalogue tucked under my arm and the letter in my hand. Granny doesn't know that I put a stamp on it and drop it into the outdoor slot at the post office all by myself. Nobody knows.

The countdown continues. According to Granny, there are now thirty days until Christmas. Smoky and I are playing in the back yard when a car pulls up in front of the hotel. For some reason, men immediately gather around it. Boys come running from all directions attracted by the commotion. Curiosity draws me toward the noisy crowd. It's a cloudy day and very cold with ice crystals on the trees. I am appalled by what is causing the excitement. Two deer are tied onto the roof of the car with thick rope twisted through their antlers, over their bodies, and around their legs, which stick up into the air. One has its head turned toward me. I stop in my tracks when I am faced with the shocking sight. Its beautiful eyes are frozen open with frost on its eyelashes and staring at me as though to ask, "Why did they do this to me? I should be running free!" I hate the hunters and the men standing around admiring the kill. I know my daddy would never do this. He doesn't own a gun and would surely say, "Let live," with a long "i" as in "alive."

There are only ten more days until Christmas, and I am now counting them down myself. Daddy is home for an entire month. It snows, and snows, and snows until the roads are blocked. For days, nobody comes into town and nobody leaves. Snowflakes do not excite me any more. The wind howls and our place is freezing cold. Daddy spends most of his time scrounging for wood to burn in the stoves. When the blizzard finally stops, the plow barrels through town. Everyone on Main Street comes out to watch and cheer as the snow furls off the blade and forms mountains on both sides of the road.

The sun is shining again, and my thoughts return to Christmas. On the morning of the fifth day before Christmas, I am awakened by loud voices. I jump off the foot of my sisters' bed, dress quickly, and hurry downstairs just in time to see Daddy pulling a spruce tree through the back door. He maneuvers it into the living room leaving a trail of dry snow on the kitchen floor and sets it in the corner. Med Sis finds a box of decorations in the cubbyhole under the stairs. Granny sits in the armchair, sips on a cup of tea, and watches us decorate the tree. I am pretty much in the way as my sisters drape a golden garland several times around the tree. Then they hang colored glass balls from its branches. My favorite decorations are the clear icicles. The last decoration to take its place on the top of the tree is a silver star. Then we all stand by Granny and admire the tree as the sun shines through the Main Street Bedroom window causing the decorations to glow and glisten. Later in the day, I wait impatiently for Granny to wake up from her nap, which she usually takes in the afternoon. After I hear her stirring, I knock and she beckons for me to come in.

"Granny, isn't the tree beautiful? But, why is it in the house? And, why is the star on top?" I ask.

Granny thinks for a moment and begins to teach me all about Christmas. "Once upon a time, people did not believe in God or Jesus. They were pagans, who worshipped different objects like the sun, the moon, animals, statues, and many other things. A festival was held in the winter to celebrate the shortest day and longest night of the year. They brought samples of their harvest into their homes as part of the celebration. Jesus' birthday is what we celebrate at Christmas. People began to bring evergreen branches and trees into their homes as part of the Christmas celebration, which was eventually combined with the existing winter festival. Over the years, they began decorating the trees and the insides and outsides of their homes, too. The star on top of the tree represents the Star of Bethlehem that shone on Baby Jesus when he was born." Granny stands up and I follow her to the globe. She points to the exact spot where Jesus was born. I am anxious to see where we live, where Frizzy and her brother are, where Big Sis lives, and where the big city is. Granny is pleased with my enthusiasm and takes great pride in pointing out where every place is in relation to where Jesus was born. I am surprised to see we live on the other side of the globe.

Then we sit on the edge of the bed as Granny continues with the lesson, "This is how the story of the birth of Jesus goes. According to Matthew 1, The Birth of Jesus, the Virgin Mary came to be with the child Jesus through the Holy Spirit; and Joseph took her as his wife, as instructed by an angel appearing to him in a dream, and in order to fulfill a prophecy. He was to care for Jesus, who was destined to save people from their sins. Matthew 2 tells a story about Jesus' birth. Jesus was born in Bethlehem and three wise men, known as Magi, came to worship him after seeing his star in the east. I think that the star was really an alignment of planets. However, in Jerusalem, the Magi asked where the king of the Jews was born. I don't think they should have had to ask questions if they were so wise. Anyway, Herod, who was king of the Jews, and his priests and teachers of the law told the Magi that Jesus was born in Bethlehem, also to fulfill a prophecy made in the Old Testament. I must question why the wise Magi would inform Herod that a possible King of the Jews had been born. They should have known that Herod would act to protect his position as king. The Magi followed the star and came to a house, not an inn or a stable. No mention of a manger in which Baby Jesus was supposed to be placed is made in this story. The Magi presented Jesus with the gifts of gold, incense, and myrrh.

Later, Herod ordered that all of the children under two years of age be killed in Bethlehem in order to protect his crown and to fulfill another prophecy. However, Jesus had been taken to Egypt in order to fulfill yet another prophecy.

After Herod died, Jesus was taken to Nazareth to fulfill even another prophecy and to protect him from Herod's son who became king. Another story is told about Jesus' birth in Luke 2. Mary and Joseph traveled from Nazareth to Bethlehem to register in the census. Mary gave birth and had to place Baby Jesus in a manger because there was no room at the inn. Again, no mention is made of a stable. The Angel of the Lord appeared to shepherds nearby informing them of the birth and telling them where to find Mary, Joseph, and the Baby. The shepherds found them and spread the word about the child. No mention of the Magi or the house is made in this story."

When I yawn, Granny allows me to lie back on her pillows and says, "I'm almost finished and just want to add a few things. The Magi and the birth of Jesus appear to be responsible for the deaths of innocent babies in Bethlehem. In the Matthew story, angels appear in dreams five times to warn or advise Joseph or the Magi about what they are to do. In Isaiah 7:13-16 and 9:6-8, a prophecy is directed to the attention of the house of David announcing that a virgin would give birth to a son. He would be named Immanuel, which means 'God with us,' and would reign on David's throne. The prophecy in Micah 5:2-5 claims that the one who would rule over Israel would come out of Bethlehem and would be its peace. In the New Testament's stories about Jesus' birth, the prophecies made in the Old Testament are conveniently fulfilled. Mary is chosen as the mother because she is a virgin, and Joseph is chosen as the father because he is from the house of David. They travel to Bethlehem for the census so that the child is born there and name him Jesus, which means 'the Lord saves.' I think the lesson to be learned here is that if you have a dream or have your fortune told or read your horoscope, don't let any of those supposed prophecies influence your actions to try to make them come true because then the prophecies can take control of you. As for angels, I've never had one appear in any of my dreams yet." Granny closes the Bible and glances at the clock on her desk. "My, it's almost time for supper," she exclaims with surprise. "You can run along now," she adds.

I have had my fill of Jesus, the Magi, the Virgin Mary, and Herod, at least, until next Christmas. The minute I leave her room, my brain replaces them with less complicated and more pleasant things like Pumpkinhead, Santa Claus, and the Christmas tree.

9

Finally, finally, finally, Christmas Eve is upon us. It is bitterly cold outside, and darkness comes early because we are approaching the shortest day and longest night of the year. Daddy builds a big fire in the box stove upstairs. After deciding which of my brown stockings is long enough to hold Pumpkinhead, I place it under the tree and notice that my sisters' socks are already there waiting for Santa. They had joked all week about who would find the biggest sock. Mom carries the coal oil lantern upstairs as she does every night.

While Daddy is home, I sleep in my sisters' room. Mom leaves the door open in order for the heat from the box stove to reach us and checks to make sure we are in bed before blowing out the lantern. The only light in the room emanates from the damper on the front of the stove that has already turned red from the logs burning inside. I kneel on my bed, say my prayers, and snuggle down under my feather tick so that even my head is covered. My thoughts are of Pumpkinhead as I am concerned about how Santa will deliver him. The pipe running from the chimney to the cookstove is too narrow for his big belly, as is the pipe descending from the roof to the big heater in the store. He surely wouldn't come down the pipe into the hot box stove upstairs. I fall asleep within minutes but wake up several times during the night and stare into the heavy darkness. I hear Daddy's grandfather's clock, which hangs behind the counter in the store, strike two times for two o'clock. The next time I hear it chime four times. Granny taught me to count them.

When I open my eyes again, daylight has barely broken. I creep downstairs carrying my felt shoes. By the time I get to the bottom stair, my feet are freezing so I stop to slip my shoes on and head straight for the Christmas tree. I can see that my stocking has a big round bulge at the toe and several lumps all the way down—those would be Pumpkinhead's head, arms, feet and tail. In blissful anticipation, I kneel in front of the tree, glance up at the star, and reach for my stocking. As I pick it up, candies and peanuts fall out of it. There are no Pumpkinhead arms or legs in the stocking, and Pumpkinhead's head is really a Christmas orange. My first thought is that there must be some horrible mistake because I couldn't have been so bad that Santa didn't think I deserved Pumpkinhead. Possibly, Pumpkinhead was too big to fit in my stocking. I search frantically under the tree and can see that my sisters' stockings are filled with candies, peanuts, and an orange, too. There are no toys anywhere under the tree. I check the kitchen stove. It's cold, but how could Santa come down that small pipe leading to the chimney? Then I run to the heater in the store. There are a few coals glowing inside, but no sign that Santa has been there either. I return to the tree in desperation and begin to make excuses for Santa. Perhaps, it is too cold for him to get here this year—besides, there is so much snow. Then I remember the reindeer with its eyes frozen open and frost glistening on its eyelashes. Maybe those reindeer on the car were Santa's. Suddenly, I begin to shiver so I grab a pillow from the sofa and Daddy's parka and then crawl into the curve of the loveseat in the store. My teeth begin to chatter so I pull the parka over my head. My profound disappointment dissipates as I drift into a deep sleep.

I awaken to laughter coming from the living room. Swinging my feet to the floor, I realize I still have my felt shoes on. The air is fringed with frost. I hear Daddy throwing some wood into the stove behind me. My thoughts immediately return to Santa, Pumpkinhead, and the reindeer with its eyes frozen open. I can't tell anyone that Santa didn't bring me Pumpkinhead because then they would be convinced that I was a really bad girl. I slowly make my way to the living room. My sisters call for me to join their nativity scene. They have placed one of my dolls in a shoebox filled with hay. Each of us is to be a wise man bringing a gift to the Baby Jesus. According to Granny, the Magi never did see Baby Jesus in the manger but I don't say anything. They begin to sing "We Three Kings." Med Sis sings first and brings gold, which is an orange. Small Sis's turn is next. She brings frankincense, which is hard candy. I go last and bring myrrh, which is a peanut.

If I were a baby, I'd want a Pumpkinhead, not those things. If the Magi were so concerned about Jesus, why didn't they bring him presents every year or send him money so he wouldn't be poor? I know it is no fun being poor, not having enough to eat, and not getting a Christmas present. At least Baby Jesus got presents. And if those presents were so expensive, why didn't Joseph sell them? After our pageant, we sit around the tree. My sisters eat the oranges and candy and throw peanuts at each other while they sing, "There goes Santa Claus right past our house again." They laugh until they cry, but I don't think it is funny.

Granny never mentions Pumpkinhead, and I hope it is because she doesn't know that I mailed the letter. I have a feeling that Santa doesn't love me, and, for that matter, neither does Jesus. I'd never sing the hymn, "Yes, Jesus Loves Me" ever again. If I were a boy, I would have gotten a real present—a gun so that I could shoot a reindeer. Furthermore, if there were a hell, it would be freezing cold and not boiling hot. The day passes slowly because we don't do anything special. Mom is waiting for Ukrainian Christmas to celebrate. I doubt that St. Nicholas, the great Ukrainian Santa, will bring me Pumpkinhead. I see a bowl of oranges, a bag of peanuts, and some hard candy under the counter and have a good idea of how our stockings got stuffed. I am so disgusted with Christmas that I go upstairs early.

I vaguely hear the others bed down for the night. Much later, I feel an unexplainable force drawing me to the entrance of the attic. A feeble attempt to retreat to the safety of my bed fails. The force is too strong, and I reluctantly approach the hole in the wall and peer to the right down the long, narrow attic. About halfway down, to my horror, the sight of the unforgettable Billy Goats Gruff's troll, cowering over a crystal ball, meets my eyes. His gnarled hands are stretched and curled over the ball but not quite touching it. He appears to be in a trance, with his ugly eyes bugged wide open, and his face twisting and shifting as if he is in pain. I don't want to look at him, but I succumb to his spell because I am now unable to move. The force is winning, and I am being drawn closer to him. I cannot imagine what will happen when that evil creature becomes aware of my presence. Surely, he will know how bad I am; and the crystal ball will tell him I didn't get Pumpkinhead for Christmas. His head begins to turn in my direction. Then, as if by some miracle, I am free to back away. My eyes open, and I discover that I am scrunched into the corner of my bed. My body is wet with perspiration, and I am overcome with nausea. The air in the room feels colder than ever. I pull the covers over my head and don't dare fall asleep again. Hours pass ever so slowly. Eventually, the alarm goes off. Under my feather tick, I wait until my sisters get out of bed, dress, and prepare to leave the room. I am right at their heels, keeping my eyes lowered to avoid looking at the entrance of the attic and what I know is inside.

Boxing Day and the next few days pass slowly. I spend the nights huddled at the foot of my sisters' bed, sneaking in after I am sure they are asleep. I can't bear to be upstairs alone or to sleep alone. Daddy senses something is wrong with me and assumes I am bored. The mail truck has arrived so he asks me if I want to accompany him to the post office. He dresses me up in my blue tweed coat with matching hat and ski pants and winds my red scarf around my head, leaving only my eyes unprotected. Taking me by my mitt-covered hand, we set off for the post office, which is just across Main Street and a few doors down. The harsh cold air immediately surrounds us. There is no wind so the smoke from the chimneys of the buildings on both sides of the street rises straight up into the sharp blue sky. My eyeballs feel as though they are freezing, and I am afraid that they might fall out of my sockets and go rolling like blue marbles on the path in front of us. The sound of the snow crunching under our boots echoes all around us. The storm door squeals from being cold as Daddy opens it, and a rush of warm air greets us as we enter.

The post-office wicket that is still closed reminds me of a little cage. Someone is sorting mail. We listen to the person slip letters, newspapers, or magazines into the boxes, which are constructed of metal and decorated with glass doors, each with a keyhole in the center. Heavier items bang on the glass after sliding into the box. We hear something slip into our box, and Daddy immediately opens it with his key. He pulls out a card indicating that there is a parcel for us.

Without warning, the cage bursts open; and a woman spouting a bumblebee's voice buzzes, "And how are you, young lady? I have a parcel for you!" I peep over the wicket counter while she peeps over the other side. I am sure that we are the same height. I nickname her "Mrs. Bee." Her husband is also short and wears bumblebee glasses similar to hers, only his lenses are dark, making him look more like a bee than she does. His wavy black hair is combed away from his forehead. He is sitting on a high stool crouched over a desk and surrounded by envelopes. As he works, I listen to the rhythm of his stamper flying from stamp pad to letters and back again, back and forth, and back and forth. Mrs. Bee appears with the parcel at the side door and hands it to me.

"Thank you very much," I exclaim as I examine it closely, shaking it and wondering if it contains Pumpkinhead. We are out the door and home again so quickly that I hardly notice the cold. While I whip off my mittens, scarf, coat, and felt boots, I call for Med Sis to help me open the parcel. She finds the scissors, places the parcel on the counter, and cuts the string. The brown paper unfolds to reveal a white box. I remove the top and push aside the tissue paper to see a beautiful doll with hair the same color as mine. She is wearing a light blue dress, matching bonnet, and black shoes. As I gently lift her from the box, her eyelids open and she looks at me. Her eyes are the same color as her dress. I name her "Blue Eyes." "Another doll! I'm really spoiled now," I whisper. Under the doll, I find a package that contains a pair of sheer nylons and a letter. Med Sis reads the letter, which is from Frizzy's brother, who writes that he wishes he could have been with us to celebrate Christmas and that he really misses us. The nylons are a gift for Med Sis, who wonders how he guessed her size. He wants me to think about him whenever I play with Blue Eyes and to never forget him. I am so overwhelmed by the thought that he cares so much about us that my eyes brim with tears. "I want to write him a thank-you letter," I sniffle. My sister finds some newsprint and an envelope while I retrieve the sheet of paper on which Granny has printed the alphabet in capital and small letters. I am able to print most of the alphabets as my sister spells the words I want to send to him. I like to make my little "g" fancy just like the ones in the reader with the picture of the troll. Med Sis adds a PS thanking him for the nylons. Daddy offers to take the letter to the post office, but I insist that I go with him. I plant a kiss on the back of the letter for good luck and drop it into the mail slot.

10

New Year's Eve arrives before I know it. We all meet at the table at the back of the store and gather around the battery radio waiting for the countdown to midnight. The station fades out occasionally, but Granny fills in its gaps of silence with her stories. I helped my sisters make paper hats in the afternoon. Mine is made out of blue crepe paper with a silver cigarette paper star pasted at the top. I place it on my head and glance in the mirror, deciding it is perfect for me.

My sisters pop corn and supply each of us with a makeshift noisemaker. Shortly before midnight, there is a dull thud at the store front door. Daddy runs to open it, and a slender black cat quickly enters accompanied by a gust of wind and blowing snow. He shuts the door after it, and

everyone fusses over the intruder except me. The countdown to the witching hour begins as the cat makes its way
toward Granny, arches its back, and begins slithering to and
fro against the hem of her skirt. As the radio announcer calls
out, "Happy New Year," my sisters begin banging spoons
against the pots and pans and blowing their whistles. Shots
are fired somewhere on Main Street while Smoky howls and
moans. I am barely conscious of the noise around me
because all of my attention is focused on the menacing glare
of the cat's eyes and the flick of its snakelike tail as Granny
reaches down to pet it. They all begin wishing each other a
Happy New Year accompanied with hugs and kisses. When
the entire ruckus dies down, Granny picks up the cat and
examines it.

"It's a female," she determines. Then looking in my
direction, she continues, "Let's call her Nancy. I know that is
one of your favorite names from the reader we are working
on now." I hesitatingly nod my approval. So Nancy is to
make her home with us, which leaves me feeling
uncomfortable. I don't like black cats. They are bad luck.

The New Year doesn't bring anything new or, at least,
nothing new that I can see. Everything is the same indoors
and the miserable weather continues outdoors. I am weary
of the cold. However, the celebration of Christmas continues
with the preparation for Ukrainian Christmas. Granny
explains that Ukrainians use a different calendar and that is
why my mother wants us to celebrate our Christmas two
weeks after English Christmas. The day before Mom's
Christmas, the snow stops and the sun comes out. Daddy
goes for the mail and comes back with a parcel from Big Sis.
We all gather around as Mom opens it. Inside are two
squares of Christmas cake that Big Sis baked herself,
packages of jelly and pudding powders, and small gifts for
everyone. Mine is a little book shaped like pair of mittens.

On the front cover is a picture of a mother cat wearing a bonnet and pushing three kittens in a baby carriage. Each of the three kittens also wears a bonnet and mittens that stick out of a blanket. I admire the mother cat's eyes, which do not at all resemble Nancy's. Granny volunteers to read the book to me so I move closer to her side on the loveseat. She begins, "Three little kittens lost their mittens, and they began to cry, "Waah, waah, waah..." I beg her to read it over and over again until I memorize the whole story.

The remainder of the day is spent helping Mom prepare the twelve meatless dishes served in honor of Jesus's twelve apostles. According to tradition, the evening meal is to begin when the first star appears. The nights are very long and it gets dark early. The table is all set. Daddy brings in some hay and arranges it neatly in a thick layer under the table and hides nuts in it for us to find after supper. Soon it is time to look for the star. The youngest person in the family must find it, so the task is up to me.

Daddy and I go outdoors several times. The sky is still clear, and the air surrounding us is so cold that we can see our breath when we speak. Finally, I spot the star and excitedly point it out to Daddy. Everyone runs out to take a look and then hurries back in to eat. Daddy lights the two blessed candles as we take our places around the table. Then we all bow our heads. Granny recites the grace that I heard her rehearsing earlier in the day. To begin the meal, we each eat a small bowlful of boiled wheat sweetened with honey and garnished with poppy seeds for good luck and prosperity. Then we help ourselves to the main course, which includes fried pickerel bought from a fisherman in town, rice and buckwheat cabbage rolls, cottage cheese and potato perogies with fried onions and sour cream, cottage cheese crepes, shredded beets with horseradish, and salad. For dessert, we indulge in a treat of prune-filled perogies. I eat until I am stuffed, as we all do. I silently give thanks to Jesus and God for making Mom so religious that she cooks so many things for the holy holiday. After the dishes are cleared off the table, we search in the hay for the nuts. Daddy cracks mine with a hammer. I prefer almonds to hazelnuts and walnuts, but my favorite is the Brazil nut.

Later at night, Granny asks, "Did you enjoy your supper?"

"It was delicious," I reply rubbing my stomach that is still full for a change. I don't care about St. Nicholas's supposed arrival. For obvious reasons, I have a pretty good idea that he won't bring me Pumpkinhead either, but I do have a question for Granny. "What are the twelve apostles?"

Granny smiles and explains, "They are the twelve men who gave up everything in order to learn from Jesus and to spread his teachings."

I know immediately who they are and blurt out, "I saw paintings of them at church. They wear long dresses, no shoes, and stare up into space. The apostles wouldn't last long teaching here because their bare feet would freeze. All they would have to say, if they showed up at our door, is that they know Jesus; and Mom would take them in, feed them, find them boots, and give them a place to sleep." Granny smiles again at my response and nods her head as she leaves the kitchen for her room. Mom's Christmas comes and goes with no sign of Pumpkinhead. I don't want her New Year to come because then Daddy will leave, but it comes anyway. I soon find myself saying good-bye to Daddy again.

I begin to think winter will never end; but one day in March, the sun comes out and melts the snow like magic. Many yards are flooded. The run-off from Main Street flows into a ditch, which is shallow in front of our place and grassy and knee-deep as makes its way out of town. I slip on a pair of Daddy's high-tops and stumble along in the shallow section of the ditch. To my amazement, I spot little fish swimming around my boots. After several attempts, I manage to catch a few before the water seeps over the top of the boots filling them to the brim. I remove them on the grass under the poplar tree and drop the fish into one boot to keep them from escaping while I run to fetch a jar.

Carefully, I tip the boot over pouring the contents into the two-quart sealer. The tiny fish struggle but are forced into the jar by the stream of water flowing like a waterfall from the boot. I watch them swim around for most of the afternoon. They are unmistakably gray, but their scales reflect the colors of the rainbow in the sun. I leave the jar outside overnight. In the morning, I am shocked to find that the jar is full of ice. However, the fish survived and are still swimming around through tunnels they kept open, I assume, by swimming around all night. I am relieved when the ice in the jar melts, and I am able to return them to the ditch and free them with Daddy's words echoing in my brain, "Let live," with a long "i" as in "alive."

The next day, a tall guy walks into town, appearing to be guided there by a spring breeze. I watch him from behind the rain barrel and decide he cannot be an apostle because he isn't wearing a dress and his feet aren't bare. Instead, he wears dark pants, a matching shirt with a pen in the chest pocket, and work boots and carries a backpack over his shoulder. To my surprise, he opens the door to our store and enters. Without his knowledge, I sneak in behind him. Mom, Granny, and my sisters seem happy to see him. I watch him gesture with his hands as he makes whispering sounds. They file into the kitchen and I follow. Mom directs his attention to me by pointing my way. He turns around, smiles like he knows me, and scoops me up lifting me until my head touches the ceiling. He repeats the act three more times as I squeal with delight. After setting me down, he removes his backpack, opens it, and gently pulls out a camera. He proudly points it at us and motions to the sofa in the living room, obviously, wanting to take pictures of us sitting on it.

I am wearing a dress that Mom sewed. The fabric has a white background scattered here and there with bunches of pansies. The top is plain with short sleeves, and the skirt flares out slightly from the waist. I run a comb through my hair and sit on the sofa with my hands clasped firmly on my lap. "Tall Guy," which I named the man when I first laid eyes on him, pulls a toy monkey out of his pocket and snaps a picture of me when I smile. I am startled by the flash of light and see spots before my eyes for a long time. He asks Mom when my dad is coming home by moving his hands around, and she holds up two fingers indicating that he will be home in two days. Tall Guy gestures excitedly and makes whispering noises while my sisters interpret his message. As far as they can understand, he will be back at noon on Sunday, after Daddy arrives, to take a family photograph. After he leaves, I ask, "Mom, what's wrong with him, and where does he live?"

"He was kicked on the side of the head by a horse when he was small. Now he is almost deaf and can't talk. He lives on a farm and walks into town and all over the place visiting people he likes," she explains.

Two days later, after waiting impatiently for Daddy, I jump up and down when I see him come around the corner with his black suitcase in one hand and rolled bag under his arm. I run toward him and we meet in front of the beer parlor. He drops his bag and suitcase and swings me up into the air. After catching my breath, I inform him that Tall Guy is coming to take our picture on Sunday. He instantly knows exactly who Tall Guy is.

An old Finnish man warms up his sauna every Saturday and charges people ten cents to use it. As my sisters prepare to leave for a bath, I ask, "What happens there?"

"We sit and sweat and wash ourselves off," answers Med Sis with a smile.

"Mom won't let me go with you and it sounds like fun," I whine.

"It's too hot for little kids like you," she replies as they walk out the door. Earlier in the morning, Daddy carried in water from the rain barrel outside and heated it up in a galvanized tub on the cookstove. I take a bath in it in the living room that is closed off from the other rooms with sheets on the doorways. I love being in the tub and soap up my entire body several times.

"If you want to get rid of the hair on your arms and legs, you must scrub hard," says Mom. I oblige and the smell of the orange soap soon fills the room. When I am finished, Mom takes her turn in my water. The girls return squeaky clean. Daddy has his sauna late in evening, but I am still awake when he comes home. His face is red and shiny, and he smells spicy like his suitcase and Frizzy's brother.

Everyone is up early the next morning. My sisters come into the kitchen with pin curls still in their hair. They made them the night before by winding dampened strands of hair around their pointer fingers, flattening them, and holding them in place with bobby pins. The pin curls were allowed dry over night. I am wearing my light blue dress. My mother looks beautiful in her burgundy dress with a black corded design on the front. She has combed her hair into waves on both sides of her head. Daddy looks handsome in a white shirt with dark pants and suspenders. After taking out their bobby pins, my sisters fuss with their hair, copying styles from a movie magazine. Then Med Sis changes into her new skirt and blouse set. Small Sis chooses to wear a flared skirt, white blouse, and colorful neckerchief.

I sit on the front step, waiting for Tall Guy; I holler when I see him coming around the curve in front of the church. Smoky runs to greet him with his stubby tail wagging in a blur. Tall Guy decides to take the picture outdoors and chooses the west side of the store for the setting of the photo. The sun is shining directly overhead in a cloud-free sky. He motions us to our places. I stand in front of Mom and Daddy, and my sisters stand beside Mom. He snaps several shots of various poses. Then we have sandwiches and a cold drink for lunch.

After Tall Guy leaves, I climb onto Daddy's lap. He shows me his new wristwatch, the first one I have ever seen! He holds it to my ear while I listen to the gentle ticking. Then he teaches me how to wind it with the tiny knob on the side. Carefully wind, wind, wind, but just until it won't wind anymore or else the spring will break. He pulls out the little knob and winds it between his fingers to make the delicate hands on its face move. After taking off the back with a small screwdriver, we examine the inside closely. I am amazed at the tiny golden wheels that move back and forth so precisely. Then he snaps the two pieces back together. As we watch the hands, he gives me a lesson on telling time. I discover that not only does the minute hand take a long time to move but that the hour hand takes forever. Daddy surprises me when he slips the watch onto my wrist. The golden band stretches like an accordion as I pull it up past my elbow and onto the top part of my arm. I help him play Solitaire while we wait for the short fat hand to move from three to four. When Daddy puts the watch back on his wrist, I run outside to play but I check with him every so often to ask for the time.

11

Daddy has been home for a week, and Easter is fast approaching. A bunny is supposed to bring me chocolate eggs. I don't think a rabbit is capable of delivering eggs to me, never mind finding or making them. Santa couldn't bring me Pumpkinhead even after I wrote him a letter, and he is a man. I have questions for Granny when she invites me into her room. As I watch her daily ritual of preparing for bed, I ask, "Please can you tell me about Easter?"

"There is more to Easter than bunnies and chocolate eggs," she remarks. "Come and sit by me on my bed. Every little girl should know what the Bible says about Easter. Remember when I told you about Jesus, and how he was born on Christmas Day? Well, Good Friday marks the day he died, and Easter Sunday is the day he rose from the dead and entered heaven to be with his Father."

"Why do they call it Good Friday, if he died on Friday?" I ask with a puzzled look on my face.

Granny smiles and exclaims, "That's a good question. Well, it's good because he supposedly died to save us from our sins—all the bad things people do. What makes them so bad is that people know they are doing something wrong but do it anyway."

"Why do they call the holiday Easter?" I ask, to keep her talking.

"I don't know; but we'll look up the word '"Easter" in my trusty Webster's dictionary," she replies as she leans over and plucks a hard-covered book with tattered corners from the top shelf of the bookcase beside her bed. She turns the pages with her white fingers treating each page as if it were a dear old friend. She continues, " E for Easter," and begins to read in a voice that sounds like she is also eager to learn something new, "'a paschal feast, originally, a pagan feast in honor of the Goddess of spring, Easter, held in April'. This is very interesting. I'm glad you asked me that question. When you go to school, be sure to ask your teacher questions because you want to learn as much as you can." She moves her watery eyes back to the page and continues to read, "'also, an annual Christian festival in commemoration of the resurrection of Jesus, held on the first Sunday after the date of the first full moon that occurs on or after March 21.' I didn't know how they arrived at the date, and why it is different every year. And, now I know. Your mom was born on March 21, but her birth certificate says March 20. We'll be celebrating Ukrainian Easter, which, like Ukrainian Christmas, is on a date different from the corresponding English holiday. The New Testament is made up of many stories in book form, some of which are named for the apostles. Remember the stories I told you about Baby Jesus from the books of Matthew and Luke? Well, we will look at those books again and also two books entitled Mark and John that tell of Jesus' death. Jesus was crucified, which means that he was stretched out on a wooden cross with his hands nailed on the ends of the arms of the cross and his feet nailed to the bottom of it. A roughly formed halo of thorns was then placed on his head. He was left to hang on the cross until he died. Pilate, the governor, wanted to free Jesus. Many Christians believe that Pilate was the one who wanted Jesus crucified."

While I think about the cross people kissed at my mother's church, Ganny finds her notebook and Bible. She clears her throat, and my lesson about the death of Jesus begins as she looks at her notes and reads, "According to Matthew 27 and 28, the people wanted Jesus crucified, saying that his blood would be on them and their children. It is difficult to believe that they turned against him because these very people brought their sick to Jesus to be healed. He even brought some of their dead back to life. The chief priests, teachers of the law, and elders also wanted Jesus to be crucified because they were jealous of him. A man named Simon from Cyrene was forced to carry Jesus's cross to Golgotha, which means 'The Place of the Skull' and was the site where Jesus was crucified. Most people believe that Jesus carried his own cross. His body was given to a rich disciple, Joseph, who wrapped it in clean linen, placed it in his tomb, and rolled a large stone in front of the entrance to the tomb. The chief priests ordered Pilate to place a seal on the stone and to post a guard there to keep the disciples from stealing the body. I wonder what gave them the idea that the disciples would steal the body when one of the commandments states, 'Thou shalt not steal'. When Mary Magdalene accompanied by another Mary arrived at the tomb, there was an earthquake. An angel, who appeared like lightning and was wearing snow-white clothing, came from the Lord and rolled the stone away saying that Jesus had risen. They were to tell the disciples to meet him at Galilee. The guards became like dead men. I recall only one guard being mentioned to begin with, and Matthew doesn't say where the other guard came from or how many there were. Jesus met the women and gave them the same message for his disciples. His disciples met him at Galilee and doubted Jesus even though they worshipped him. Jesus sent them to make disciples in all nations, which is strange to me, since the disciples didn't seem to be very faithful to him and even doubted him."

"I like the story," I chirp with enthusiasm, encouraging her to keep on.

I smile when she continues, "According to Mark 15 and 16, the chief priests envied Jesus and they, along with the elders, the teachers of the law, and a crowd of people, called for Pilate to crucify Jesus. He handed Jesus over to the soldiers to be crucified. Simon was forced to carry the cross, as in Matthew; but in this story, the two Marys, Salome, and many other women from Jerusalem attended the crucifixion. Joseph placed the body in a tomb, which was not specified as Joseph's in this story, wrapped it in linen, and rolled the stone against the entrance. Mary saw where Jesus' body was placed and on the first day of the week she brought spices to anoint it. The stone was rolled away, and a man dressed in a white robe was sitting there. He told the women to inform Peter and the disciples to meet Jesus in Galilee. Nobody believed Mary Magdalene. Then Jesus appeared in a different form that is not described, and they still didn't believe. Then he appeared to eleven disciples and told them to preach about the creation. He gave them the power to drive out demons, heal people, speak in new tongues, hold snakes, and drink poison and not be harmed. Then Jesus was taken to heaven and sat on the right hand of God. No explanation is given about how this last statement came to be known by them. Are you getting tired little one? I can tell you the remaining stories tomorrow."

"Oh, no, Granny. My mother likes Jesus so much that I want to hear all about him," I whisper not wanting to interrupt the flow of the stories.

Granny proceeds, "According to Luke 23 and 24, Pilate tried to spare Jesus but the chief priests, rulers, and people demanded Jesus' crucifixion. Simon carried the cross again in this story. Joseph wrapped the body in linen and placed it in the tomb but did not roll the stone into the entrance.

When the women came, they found the stone moved anyway. In this story, it was two men in clothes like gleaming lightning who gave the disciples their message to go to Galilee. Peter entered the tomb and saw strips of linen. Jesus appeared to women on their way to the village of Emmanus. Jesus explained to them that the events of his death are revealed in the Scriptures and that he had to suffer to attain glory. He also explained this to his disciples who were at first afraid that he was a ghost. Through Jesus, they were made to understand the Scriptures in which was written all that would happen to him. Then he was taken up to heaven."

Granny pauses for a moment and smiles saying, "There is one more long story to tell about his death, and it is from John 19-21. Pilate stood by Jesus; but the Jews wanted him crucified because he claimed to be the Son of God. The soldiers took him; and, in this story, Jesus was said to have carried his own cross instead of Simon. As in the other books, the soldiers bid on Jesus's garments in order to fulfill the Scripture. After Jesus died, a soldier pierced Jesus's side with a spear. Water and blood flowed from the wound. This event also occurred to fulfill the Scripture. In this story, another man helped Joseph with the body wrapping it in linen with 75 pounds of myrrh and aloes. Jesus was laid in a tomb, not because it was Joseph's, but because it was new and because it was the Jewish day of Preparation, and the tomb was nearby making its use convenient. Nothing is said about the stone's being used to seal the entrance in this book; but, when only one Mary came to the tomb, the stone was moved and the body was missing. She informed the disciples about what had happened. This story mentioned a folded burial cloth from Jesus's head next to the linen. They did not know that Jesus was to rise from the dead according to the Scripture. This time, two angels dressed in white talked to Mary from inside the tomb. Then Jesus appeared, and she thought he was the gardener. There was no message to meet him in Galilee. He appeared to his disciples, who were hiding from the Jews, and gave them the Holy Spirit and power to forgive sins. A week later, Jesus appeared to his disciples even though the doors of the house were locked. Thomas felt Jesus's wounds. After that, Jesus performed miraculous signs to convince them to believe. Jesus appeared for the third time to his disciples by the Sea of Tiberias. They did not recognize him at first. He told them where to cast their net, and they caught 153 fish without breaking the net. This convinced them that he was Jesus. Nothing was said about Jesus's being taken up to heaven; but the next book, Acts 1, says that Jesus was taken up before them until a cloud hid him from sight." Granny paused and then added in a condescending tone, "Each story of Jesus's crucifixion becomes more detailed than the one before it. They are all different, yet each is supposed to be true. I don't know if I can accept that."

Granny's voice drones on. I thought I could listen to her forever, but my eyes are getting heavy. When I open them again, I am in my bed upstairs. Bright rays of sunshine are streaming through the Main Street windows. I vaguely remember hugging Daddy as he carried me upstairs and put me to bed. Thank goodness I'm dressed and don't have to spend any more time up here alone than I have to. I slip out of bed and scoop up my shoes. Then I side-step my way along the wide door that divides the two rooms and blocks the view of the entrance to the attic when it rests open against my bed. "I would like to roll a stone in front of that entrance," I whisper. Then I tiptoe quickly out of Granny's room and then through Mom's, wanting to look back, but I don't dare. I run halfway down the stairs and sit down to put on my shoes while I peer through the little window in the stairwell. I look out across the store, but it is deserted.

As I make my way down the remaining stairs, I hear voices coming from the kitchen. Then I see Granny and my two sisters sitting at the table with candles in front of them. Mom is standing at the side of the table holding a stick and winding some string around one end of it. "Come here, Johnny. I'll show you how to make Easter eggs," Med Sis says. "I'm working on one now. I take this special pen that Mom made. She has attached a piece of tin that is shaped to funnel down to a point for drawing. I heat the point in the candle flame and dip it into the beeswax like this. The wax melts and is sucked up into the rolled tin. Then I draw on the egg allowing the wax to cover what I want to be white for now."

Med Sis is a good artist and draws two beautiful flowers, one at each end of the egg, and adds some lines and fancy designs. "Now I'll put the egg in this yellow dye and cover whatever I want to be yellow with wax. Powered dyes are dissolved in water and vinegar to make the colors adhere to the egg." Several jars stand along the far side of the table. She lowers the egg into the jar of yellow dye with a spoon and leaves it in there for a while. Then she pulls it out with the spoon and examines it to see if it is the right shade. She repeats the procedure a couple of times. When she is satisfied with the color, she wipes the egg with a cloth and covers the centers of the flowers and some of the diamond shapes with wax. I can see the white lines, which she had drawn first, and the yellow centers and designs. Then she dips the egg in red dye and covers the petals with wax. The leaves are done in green, and the last color is black. When she is finished, Mom places the egg carefully on a pan in the oven. The wax melts and runs off the egg leaving behind the colored flowers and designs. Mom rubs the egg with varnish to make it shine.

I am allowed to practice on a cracked egg and hold the point over the flame, press it into the wax, and begin to draw a line on it. To my dismay, some of the hot wax drips onto my pinkie finger. I want to scream, but I don't want the stick to be taken away from me so I try to keep a straight face as I continue to make lines and circles. Then Granny invites me over to her side saying, "My hands shake because I'm old and yours shake because you're young. Perhaps, together we can turn out a decent egg. Let's make a cross on two sides of the egg." She draws the crosses and lets me fill them in with wax. "Now we'll make a wreath of thorns around the center of the egg." She draws the outline for the thorns and places the egg in orange and then in green dye to make brown. Again, my job is to fill in the outline with wax. We also make blue teardrops and red drops of blood around the crosses on each side of the egg and finish it with black dye. "This isn't a very happy Easter egg," she remarks. "Let's make another one, and we'll put whatever you want on it." When our happy Easter egg is finished, it has a white bunny on each side and a garland of white daisies with yellow centers and green leaves running lengthwise around it. The bunnies have red-dot eyes and pink inside their long ears.

"I like the happy Easter egg better than the sad one," I comment, admiring it proudly.

"I do, too," agrees Granny. "I don't know why people in the olden days thought that pain and suffering were so wonderful."

As we clear off the table and place the egg-making materials into a cardboard box, Mom looks at my sisters and says, "You will be going to confession on Saturday morning, and then I'm taking the food to be blessed to the church at night." They don't appear to be too thrilled about the idea.

"Can I confess with them?" I ask.

"You're still too young," she replies.

Envious of my sisters, I ask, "Well, what kind of sins do I have?"

"The priest just asks kids to think about their sins that would be something like not listening to their parents or not telling the truth," she explains.

12

The next morning, I am looking for Daddy and almost bump into him as he is coming in the front door. He has been at the corner store where many of the elderly men meet daily, sitting on a bench in the middle of the building to smoke and gossip. Daddy informs us that a Summer Tot Wishing Well Contest has begun to raise money to buy parts to fix the town well. Anyone can bring a picture of a child to the store, and it will be assigned to a collection jar. People will be encouraged to drop money into the jar of their choice to support their favorite tot. Kids entered must be less than eight years old. The jar containing the most money on the first day of summer will determine the winner. A prize is to be presented to the lucky tot on the first Friday after June 21.

Med Sis leaves the kitchen and soon reappears with a picture of me wearing my plaid suit. She takes my hand and we walk to the store. We enter quietly and come face to face with the old men sitting on the bench. I avoid their staring eyes. My gaze overlooks them and comes to rest on a rack of fruit. Bunches of bananas, clusters of enormous grapes, and glowing oranges are lined up vertically on a slanted case that is divided into three sections with slats of wood. Closing my eyes, I try to imagine how sweet those grapes would taste. I open them slightly; and, from the corner of my eye, I watch an old man's bony yellow fingers place shreds of tobacco on cigarette paper and awkwardly roll it with trembling hands. He licks the paper with his brown tongue and expertly places the finished product between widely-spaced, stained jagged teeth. Swiftly striking a wooden match, he lights the cigarette, which flares up wildly, and takes a quick drag as he watches us with squinty eyes peering though the thick cloud of smoke as he exhales. It is not a pretty sight.

We wait patiently while the person ahead of us places a large order. The storekeeper is a portly man with a square face and dark hair combed away from his forehead in waves so perfectly formed it appears as though he has just removed his wave clips. He is wearing a white shirt and dark pants with wide black suspenders. As he places items into a brown bag, he lists them on a narrow pad. A lengthy roll of brown paper whirls noisily as he pulls out the amount he needs and tears it neatly on the cutting blade. Then he yanks on a strand of string that spins off a large spool suspended above the counter. He winds the string several times around his pinkie finger and snaps it with the longest fingernail I have ever seen. I watch it as he twists the string around the parcel a couple of times and ties a knot and bow on top. He places the package in the bag, which the customer picks up as he moves away.

My sister hands the storekeeper the picture, and he motions for us to join him in front of the window. Several jars are already lined up on the sill. He grabs a jar lined with white paper from behind the counter and slips my picture in between the outside of the jar and the paper lining. After securing it with a lid with a slot in the middle, he sets it down at the end of the row of jars. He lifts the other jars up, one by one, and turns the pictures toward us in order to let us view them. One, in particular, catches my eye. The little girl is wearing a white dress and a large white bow in her blonde hair. She reminds me of other girls; the one at the concert, the girl in the picture at church, and the one wearing a brace on the charity pamphlet. He shakes the jar and my hear sinks when I hear coins jingle inside. I feel that everyone will choose to put money in her jar. My sister thanks him. As we leave the store, I turn to take a look at my jar at the end of the line.

"Let's go and see the well before we go home," suggests Med Sis. As we approach the well located in the center of town, we can both see that it is in need of repair. The pump stands in front of the theater on a raised wooden platform, surrounded by weather-beaten railing . The theater has been closed for the winter but will reopen in a couple of weeks. A generator supplies power to the theater. I climb the rounded and highly polished cement steps to the door and look up at a poster featuring a cowboy riding a horse, followed by a red dog. In the background stands a pretty blonde young woman wearing a white dress. I want to see the movie, and my sister must have read my mind because she says, "You are young enough to get in for free." She crouches down at the top of the steps in front of the hand-railing constructed of metal piping, grabs it, and swings through the opening to land on the sidewalk. Then it is my turn, and I hurl my body forward copying her movements. We repeat the routine until we grow tired of the game and head for home. When she opens the front door, Nancy bolts out and runs around the corner of the store.

"I'm going to follow her," I yell.

"Don't slip off the path. There are deep holes filled with water from the run-off," Med Sis hollers after me, as I catch a glimpse of Nancy disappearing behind the outhouse. I speed up and spot her again as I pass the rock. I don't want to talk to Big Brother. He'll know for sure that I was so bad that Santa never brought me Pumpkinhead.

Beyond the rock stands the small log barn that belongs to us. I never ventured out this far before. The barn door is ajar, and Nancy enters, so I follow. My eyes need time to adjust to the darkness. I open the door wider to let in more light, and now I can see a half-wall that divides the barn into two stalls. As I make my way to the end of the far stall, I stumble and almost fall into a manger. It is a timely object of interest that I am required to examine because it reminds me of Baby Jesus. The manger is splattered with dried cow pie and filled with dirty hay. I hope I will never have to sleep in one. Nancy is nowhere to be seen, but I notice a ladder nailed to the wall in one corner so I climb it and enter the loft. Rays of light drift through cracks between the logs. Wooden boxes, each containing a nest, line the walls. Feathers float into the air as I hurry back to the ladder. Bending over, I grab the end of it and try to swing my foot onto the top rung but grow dizzy as I look down. Scrambling back, I wonder how I am going to get out. Desperately I search the loft for a means of escape. The outline of a door formed by light peeping through uneven spaces around it offers some hope. By running my fingers around the edge, I find a hook, lift it, and push on the door causing it to swing open. I poke my head out and imagine I am a bird in its nest high up in a tree. The view is spectacular! I am able to survey the entire alley behind the hotel. To my left, looms the rock. The remains of a foundation jut out of the grass next to the barn indicating that it was larger at one time. Suddenly, I feel the urge to jump. Without a doubt, I would rather do that than climb down the ladder. I crouch down and spring forward. With my skirt flaring out like a parachute around me, I land perfectly on the soles of my feet. I am compelled to try it again and climb the ladder. This time I flap my arms pretending to be a bird when I jump and wonder if birds get the same feeling low down in their stomachs when they land. I practice jumping several more times before I hear my sister calling me as she runs down the path toward me. "What are you doing? You could break your neck or something. Hurry up! Let's move because it's getting dark," she snaps as she grabs my hand. I can jump as well as any boy, I think proudly, as I run along trying to keep up with her. Nancy is gone, and I couldn't care less.

I must report to Granny, who is already in her nightgown. "I saw a manger in the barn today. It was covered with cow pie. Why would God let Baby Jesus sleep in a stinky manger? Why would God let him be tortured and die on the cross, and why would God let him be poor? It's no fun being poor. I'd like to have lots of money so I could buy things out of the catalogue. Then Mom wouldn't have to sew my dresses, and I could buy all the things I want to eat. Granny, can you tell me more about Jesus, please?" I manage to also ask even though I am almost out of breath.

Granny grants me my wish and begins another lesson saying, "The Bible contains two parts, The Old Testament and the New Testament. The Old Testament is also known as the Torah and is the Book of the Jews. The Torah was so sacred to the Jewish men that women weren't even allowed to touch it. Women were required to do as much as possible for the men so that they would have free time to study the Torah. The men held debates and competitions to prove who knew the most about the Torah and their beliefs. The way the story goes is that the Jews were forced out of their land and were waiting for a deliverer, or liberator, to free them and lead them back to their Promised Land. They called this deliverer the Messiah. The Jews still don't believe that Jesus is the Messiah even though he was Jewish. However, the Christians, whose Book is the Gospel or New Testament, agree that Jesus is the Messiah." Granny glances at her clock and exclaims, "It's time for supper so I guess that's it for today's lesson." She places the Bible on the desk and turns her back for a second giving me opportune time to stick out my finger and touch the book that contains the text of the sacred Torah. Then I smile my innocent smile as we walk into the kitchen together. After supper, Mom chats with Granny while I play with Smoky.

My sisters and I go upstairs early to prepare for church the next day. I watch Med Sis pin curl her hair as she leans back against her pillows and looks into a round mirror that she balances on her stomach by propping it up against her bent knees. While she winds strands of hair around and around her finger, thoughts of Jesus, the Gospel, the Torah, Easter, and the crucifixion whirl around and around in my head until I fall asleep.

13

The dreaded day of confession is upon us. Everyone fasts in the morning, even me, because I never eat breakfast, anyway, which means that I fast every day. Then we are on our way to church. I sit beside mom and wait anxiously for my sisters to have their turn with the priest. Finally, Med Sis ventures out to the front. As with all the others, the priest drapes the end of his sash over her head and leans close to hear what she has to say. Through the tassels at the end of the sash, I can hear them mumbling back and forth but am unable to make out one word of her confession, let alone one of her sins. To my disappointment, the same results apply to Small Sis's confession. The last person to confess is a frail old woman wearing a large hearing aid. Hers is a special confession because she is convinced she will die soon. No attempt is made to stop her as she enters the room at the side of the altar, and the priest inadvertently follows her.

The congregation, sitting quietly, is startled by the woman's extremely loud, wobbly voice moaning, "I have no sins! I have no sins! I HAVE NO SINS!" Then the members glance at each other trying not to laugh, but many snicker under their breath. The priest comes out looking embarrassed. She certainly will have no problem getting her way or being heard in heaven, or so I think. At least, and I must admire her for it, she made it into the room behind the altar without having to dust or clean.

When we return home, Mom bustles about the kitchen preparing for the blessing of food at church in the evening. She sets a large basin on a white tablecloth and covers the basin with a yellow cloth. Then she places a "paska" in the middle of it—paska is a special type of Ukrainian Easter bread. Mom baked several round loaves of it the day before. I watched her knead the yellow dough dotted with raisins. She decorated the tops of the loaves with strands of braided dough. My treat was to taste some of the leftovers clinging to the bowl. It was sweet and yummy. Around the paska, she arranges a dish of butter decorated with spikes of cloves, a jar of pickled beets and shredded horseradish, a small pork roast, a ring of garlic sausage, boiled eggs, and Easter eggs—including two that Granny and I decorated. She gathers the ends of the tablecloth together and ties them into a knot. The basin becomes a basket and the knot its handle.

Soon Mom and I are back at the church. She places her basket along with many others lining both sides of the red carpet that leads to the altar. The women pay for blessed candles that they light and gently force into the centers of their paskas. Darkness is beginning to fall so the candles provide the only lighting in the church, illuminating the faces of the women as they stand behind their baskets, and casting huge shadows of their bodies against the walls and up the domed ceiling of the church. The priest rushes in from behind the altar like a bat wearing a black cape, which hovers and flaps over a black suit. He begins to sing in his loud, whiny voice as he dips a silver object shaped like a drumstick into a matching goblet and flicks holy water at each of the baskets. After some more hurried singing and praying, the ceremony is over. The women leave money for the blessing of the food and gather up their baskets as they file out of the church.

The Easter bunny proves to be no more reliable than Santa Claus. There are no chocolate eggs or bunnies to be found on Easter Sunday, but I don't mind as I really didn't expect any. Instead, there is plenty of blessed food to eat. I make sure to have my share of paska and beets with horseradish, which is my favorite.

The morning after Daddy leaves for work I wake up in a sweaty ball . I was tormented by another nightmare featuring the ugly troll. I hate him so much but am determined not to let him get the best of me. My sisters still have another week of Easter break left. I hear my mother calling me and hurry downstairs. "Run to the store for Med Sis," she orders.

"Why can't she go herself?" I mumble.

"She isn't feeling good, and you can have a box of popcorn if you go." She hands me a slip of paper and off I run. Thank goodness it's early—the old men aren't there yet. The storekeeper reads the note and grabs a flat box wrapped in plain brown paper from a low shelf and drops it into a paper bag. Then he takes out a long bung of balogna, cuts off a chunk, and places it on a square of wax paper on the scale. I watch his pinkie finger with its long fingernail as he wraps the meat. He proceeds to jiggle several boxes of popcorn until he is satisfied that the one he chooses contains a good prize and hands it to me over the counter. I take the brown bag and stop for a minute to check the contest jars. He picks mine up and gently shakes it. The jingling of coins makes me smile. I hop and skip all the way home carrying the bag of groceries, which I drop off in the kitchen. Then I sit on the back step with Smoky by my side and decide it's time I named the storekeeper "the Man with the Fingernail." He made the right choice for me—inside the box of popcorn, I find a small brown furry monkey with moveable arms and legs. It is almost as cute as Pumpkinhead but not quite. I eat my pink popcorn sharing it with Smoky and think about my sixth birthday that is coming soon. I am also looking forward to attending my first movie on Friday night.

I watch Med Sis leave for the movie from behind the rain barrel. She meets some friends when she crosses the street, and I follow far behind. They pay for their tickets in the lobby. I admire the girl sitting behind the curved glass window as she tears their tickets and then lets me in for free. The air is filled with the smell of popcorn. I watch the girl behind another counter shovel it into boxes as it flows out of a machine.

My sister spots me just as she is about to enter the theater. She looks annoyed, only for a second; and motions for me to squeeze in ahead of her. She tells me to sit in the front with the other kids. I make my way past rows of plush chairs with curved arm rests and rows of wooden benches to the front row and sit down in the middle to the left of the aisle. I look back to watch people hurrying in to find a seat. Everyone is talking. I notice a few empty seats in front of Med Sis. Without warning, the lights go out as a hush falls over the theater. For a moment, there is complete darkness. Then the screen lights up. I have never before seen anything so brilliant. My attention focuses on a man with a narrow face and mustache to match. He sits in front of a microphone and, in a matter-of-fact manner, announces the news. As he speaks, vehicles speed around and men in suits and trench coats strut stiffly and swiftly along city streets as the film switches into fast motion. Then Woody Woodpecker appears in a flash of color in the first cartoon I have ever seen. I follow his beak with my eyes as he pecks out his name on a slab of wood and I cheer along with the other kids. I wish the cartoon could go on forever, but soon the movie begins. Cowboys with guns shoot Indians, and Indians with arrows shoot cowboys and pioneers. People are scalped and burned at the stake. I am pretty upset with the killing and make my way to the empty seat in front of Med Sis. My daddy would say, "Let live," with a long "i" as in "alive." I lean my head on my arm and close my eyes to all that is happening on the screen. When I open them again, the lights are on and "God Save the King" is playing. My sister grabs my arm and steers me through the swarm of people leaving the theater. I can't wait to get home and into bed. I fall asleep wondering what happened to the girl in the white dress but must admit to myself that I don't really care.

14

The days before my birthday pass quickly. The evenings are warm and long, and kids from school often gather in front of our place. I sneak into the group of my sisters' friends to play games using the big tree in our yard as home base. We play "Red Light," "Hide-and-Go-Seek," and "Dodge Ball." My birthday comes, but there is no cake or presents. One morning, Granny asks me if I want to walk to the post office with her as I often do. She claims her mail by "general delivery" at the wicket. Mrs. Bee hands her a letter which she inspects closely, confirming that it is from her great niece out west. When we get home, she sits down on the edge of her bed, opens the letter, and begins to read it to herself. She informs me that her niece is inviting her to stay with her. I can't believe Granny would ever move away, but she decides it might be wise for her to spend the winter out west where the weather is warmer. I don't want her to know how upset I am with the news. "I might go for a while, but I promise I will be back," she vows. Changing the subject because she notices the disappointment in my face, she continues with a smile, "I have something for you for your birthday, even though it is a little late." As she hands me her dictionary, she says, "The print is too small for my weary eyes. Whenever you look up a word in it, I want you to think about me. You must always be interested in words." As she speaks, I allow the pages of the dictionary to flip through my fingers recognizing letters of the alphabet that Granny taught me. I am overwhelmed by the fact that I will, one day, read the words and their meanings. "I also want you to have something else," she adds as she pulls open the drawer of the small table and lifts out a box decorated with yellow and red tulips. As she removes the lid I move closer to see what is inside. She unfolds blue tissue paper to reveal two golden hair combs. "I wore these when I was a young lass being courted by my first beau whom I eventually married. When you miss me, I want you to wear them like this." She places one above my ear and zigzags it into place so that it holds my hair away from my forehead and repeats the same procedure with the other matching comb. "Now you look like my little angel with a golden halo around your head." I admire myself in the mirror, agreeing with her wholeheartedly. Then she places the dictionary in the box. I don't know how to begin to thank her for the precious gifts.

I hug her and, with tears in my eyes, I whisper, "I love you, and I'm so glad you're my granny. I will never forget you." I proudly wear the combs for the rest of the day and then hide them in the box under my bed. My sixth birthday is over, and I fall asleep with the fear gnawing at my insides that Granny might leave.

One Sunday, a couple of weeks later, I am feeling bored and restless. I hate Sundays because there is nothing to do, and the day always seems so long. I search until I find an old mail-order catalogue and a pair of scissors. Cutting out pictures of furniture is one of my favorite pastimes. As usual, I arrange the cutouts to form a kitchen, living room, nursery, bedrooms, and bathroom. I am in the process of snipping out a daddy for the family when I am startled by my mother, who crept up behind me. She snatches the scissors and yanks them out of my hand. "You know that you're not supposed to cut on Sunday," she snaps angrily and marches away. I am upset but determined to finish the family. I find a straight pin in the sewing machine and experiment on a shirt I have chosen for the daddy. It matches his size and pose so I prick holes around the outline with the pin. I intend to force out the shirt along the pinholes, but it tears when I try to pop it out. Disappointed with the attempt, I decide it is best to finish the project when I can use the scissors again.

I venture outside and sit on the front step. Smoky is resting at the corner of the lot and comes over to lie at my feet. It is a dull day but very warm—I thought Sundays were supposed to be sunny. I spot a girl walking on the other side of the street. When she turns the corner, I follow her and end up in the playground behind my mother's church. The girl watches me from the corner of her eye as she sits on a swing, hanging onto its chains which run up to an iron bar connecting the four swings to tall posts. Then she speaks to me. "Come here, and I'll push you." I climb onto the wooden seat. She grasps both chains, pulls me back, and lets me go. "Pull back on the chains, and stretch your legs out when you are going up. Then pull your feet back when you are coming down, and you'll keep going by yourself." I am surprised at how well her method works. She also teaches me how to stand up and pump. Swinging helps cool us off. Then we spend time on the teeter-totter. She must sit closer to the middle of the plank because she is heavier than I am. Later, we scour the grounds searching for flat rocks suitable for playing hopscotch. I watch patiently as she draws the squares and rectangles in the damp dirt in the shade of a long low building. When she is finished, we throw our special rocks and play—hop, hop, hop on one leg; split on two; hop on one; split on two; turn around; and back again. We hop around for a long time, mesmerized by the game. I am thirsty and hot even though the sun has not yet poked through the cloud cover. Finally, the girl decides it is time for her to leave. We head for home with each of us walking in opposite directions.

I can hardly wait to tell Granny about my learning to swing and play hopscotch. After bursting through the front door, I dash through the store and into the kitchen making my way to the beige enamel pail first. I grab the long-handled dipper. It has a chip at the bottom that matches the one at the bottom of the pail. To my dismay, the pail is nearly empty. I tip it carefully so as not to rile up the sand and dirt at the bottom and manage to scoop up a satisfactory amount. The water is warm but it's better than nothing. I gulp it down then allow the dipper to slide back into the pail. Running through the living room, I slow my pace before I enter Granny's room. I don't hear her call to me as usual, and I sense something is wrong. I look in but she is nowhere to be seen. Her bonnet is gone from the mirror spindle; there is no bible on her night table; and her black coat, dresses, and shoes are not in the closet. The cane is also missing from the knob on the Main Street door. I panic when I notice that her suitcase is not on the top shelf of the closet. As I whirl around, I almost bump into Med Sis who asks, "Where were you? Granny's great niece came to get her. Granny waited to say goodbye to you for as long as she could. They had a long trip ahead of them."

"Oh," I answer in a small voice, "I was at the playground." I turn around in disbelief and mumble, "How can I live without Granny?" as I stumble up the stairs, not caring that I will be there alone. Then I fumble under the bed for the box Granny gave me and realize I still have my hopscotch stone in my hand so I slip it into the box. Clutching the box to my chest, I hurry out of the bedroom, down the stairs, and back to the Main Street Bedroom. I open it with trembling fingers, take out the combs, and slide them into my hair. Then, holding the dictionary close, I allow my face to fall deep into her pillow. Tears will not come. I welcome sleep intoxicated by the sweet scent of Granny's silver hair, which surrounds me.

It's time for my body to wake up, but my mind doesn't want to. My eyelids are so heavy that I have to force them open. I am faced with unanswerable questions, who will be my granny now? who will teach me? and, who will read to me? After moping around all day, I decide to turn to Big Brother. I don't care if he knows I was so bad that Santa didn't bring me Pumpkinhead. I slowly remove the combs from my hair, place them into the box with the dictionary, and slide the box under Granny's bed. I make my way to the big rock with my feet crushing the spring grass as I create a new path. I wonder if Big Brother is still there. I have ignored him for too long and feel guilty. As I scramble onto the rock, he welcomes me, "So it's you again, Johnny."

I utter a sigh of relief and reply, "I guess you know Granny is gone." There is a long pause.

Then he breaks the silence saying, "I told you that you will have to get used to good-byes. You should be happy that Granny was here for you at the right time. She taught you so much. Besides, she promised you she will be back; and Granny always keeps her promises. I know you miss Frizzy, too. Remember the thank-you letter you wrote to her brother? Well, he will treasure it and keep it in his bible for years. One day, you will get it back."

Nothing more is said, and I am somewhat comforted by my surroundings as I stare at the grove of poplars ahead of me. Newly sprouted leaves rustle occasionally in the gentle breeze. The air smells fresh and clean, and the sky is beginning to clear. It is still daylight, but I know it is getting late because I feel tired. Tomorrow will be another day, a new day. With my chin up, I make my way back to the house and up the stairs. I can't fall asleep and decide it's because I must pray to God. I wait until I am sure everyone else is asleep. Then I rise up, kneel by my bed, and ask God to grant me one wish—that I will never be any trouble to anyone. Even as I pray, I believe the act may be useless. In the back of my mind lingers the reality that things would be so much better for me if I were only born a boy.

For days, I spend most of my time lying on Granny's bed or in the store under the far counter where the two parts form an "L" beneath the Main Street window. I welcome the darkness it offers and lose myself in my own peaceful world—nobody knows where I am and nobody cares. Time after time, I find myself being drawn to the playground where I spend hours swinging higher and higher. I draw a hopscotch outline in front of our store. Girls passing by often stop to play with me. I practice with a purpose throwing my special stone so that it lands perfectly and hopping so that my feet stay inside the lines. If I do things right maybe, just maybe, Granny will come home.

15

I miss the sound of Granny's voice and I often sit on the armchair near the doorway between the living room and kitchen in order to listen to conversations my mother has with the many friends and relatives who stop by. One of her daily visitors is a tall woman with skinny legs, which are always covered with brown stockings. She wears cotton dresses with hems that fall to just below her bony knees.

The skin on her face is brown and wrinkled and matches her stockings. She wears a straw hat to keep her face from getting darker from the sun. I call her "Hattie." She insists she is French, but Mom claims she is really a descendent of the Indians who live on the reservation to the north. She speaks English with a strange accent enhanced with her own vocabulary and stamps her feet on the floor whenever she laughs. After Mom brews a pot of tea, they sit and visit while munching on toast, cake, or cookies. Then Hattie leaves our place to visit other people in the neighborhood and carries on with gossiping and snacking. Mom suspects that it is her way of getting out of cooking for herself.

One day, I overhear Hattie and my mother discussing the Wishing Well contest. According to Hattie, the name of the winner will soon be announced. Talk about town is that the girl wearing the white dress and the white bow in her hair will surely be the one.

The weather has been especially hot all day. When I follow my sisters up to bed at night and they open the door, the heat from the upper floor seeps down the stairs enveloping me in what feels like a steamy blanket. Med Sis immediately throws open the north door and walks onto the balcony. The air outside is so still that no breeze can possibly enter the bedrooms. They decide to sleep on the balcony and proceed to carry out bedding. There is no room for me, they insist. I refuse to sleep in our bedroom alone so, wearing only my panties, I crawl into my mother's bed and cover myself with the thin sheet. I lie still for a few minutes, but the heat makes me restless. As I toss and turn, I begin to pray to God to help me win the wishing well contest. I don't kneel by the bed because I don't want my sisters to see me praying. When I am done, I hear them whispering so I creep out of bed and move closer to the doorway. I overhear Small Sis saying, "I walked over to where Frizzy used to live today, and I met this good-looking guy. He was sitting on a white horse and let me pet it. We talked for quite a while. He lives on a farm three miles from town and rode in for a haircut. I just knew when I looked into his blue eyes that he is the one for me and that I am going to marry him one day even though he is nine years older than I am." I picture the young man on the white horse; and a story Granny read to me comes to mind, resulting in my decision to dub him "the White Knight."

Wondering what is keeping my mother, I tiptoe down half of the stairs to the window in the stairwell. Even though it is late, there is still enough light for me to survey the store below. I observe my mom's silhouette in front of the Main Street windows. She is behind the counter and bent over the till, rummaging through it. I hear coins jingle as she drops them into her apron pocket. When she turns away from the till, I sense she is coming to bed. I silently dash up the stairs, hop into bed, and pretend to be fast asleep when she sinks into the mattress next to me.

The next day, late in the afternoon, Med Sis runs to the store because she wants to know who won the contest. Within minutes, she bursts into the kitchen hollering as she whirls me around, "You won. You are the now the Wishing Well Princess, and you have to claim your prize at the theater before the movie tomorrow tonight." My mother is smiling. I have never before seen her look so happy. I feel kind of strange wondering if all the praying I did the night before made me win the contest.

In the morning, I notice that the weather has cooled considerably from the day before. Mom figures it hailed west of town. A strong wind gives us some much-welcomed relief from the recent heat wave. I am able to wear my green and yellow plaid skirt and jacket to claim my prize at the theater. I wait with Smoky on the front step for my family as they get dressed. Then my mother, sisters, and I walk to the theater and sit together on the plush seats. I perch nervously on mine, with my feet dangling above the floor, and eagerly observe the organizers of the contest scurrying about on the stage. My heart begins to pound when the main lights go out, and only the stage lights remain on. A baldheaded man calls out my name inviting me to come up on stage. My sisters chant, "Go, go."

"Go, Johnny, go!" I whisper to myself as I muster up enough courage to leave my seat and make my way up the aisle. Then I follow a robust woman, wearing a blue and white striped dress, up the side stairs and onto the stage. She places a gold crown on my head while the people in the audience hoot, clap, and whistle. The man shakes my hand and presents me with my prize—a doll that is almost my height. It is wearing a white dress decorated with white lace and matching bonnet. Its eyes stare at me as I hug it.

Everyone cheers and laughs as I struggle slowly off the stage with my prize. She isn't Pumpkinhead, but we immediately form a bond. Now I will be considered really, really, really spoiled as I have another doll to add to my collection. I am escorted back to where my family is sitting. They examine my crown and doll during the speech session. The baldheaded man promises that the well will be as good as new when repairs are completed within the next couple of days.

My sisters stay for the movie, but I decide to leave with my mother. She reaches for my hand and squeezes it gently as we make our way down the theater steps. We are greeted by sunshine. When my eyes adjust to the light, I look up at my mother's, which are beaming even more brightly than the sunshine. In words tinged with a slight Ukrainian accent, she explains, "I wanted you to win. I wanted our family to get something special. This morning I took all of the change from the till and put it in your jar. Don't tell anyone." I stare at her in disbelief. All along, I thought she didn't care about me. A lump forms in my throat and I can't speak. As I hang onto the doll with one arm and clutch its hand in mine, my other hand tightens around my mom's as we walk. I feel so close to her at that moment as I accept the fact that it wasn't my praying to God, but rather, my mom's hard-earned money that made my winning possible.

When we enter the kitchen, I sit the doll on a chair. Then Mom and I have the opportunity to examine the crown more closely. It is a five-pointed band made out of cardboard with five large stones, each encircled with gold metal and attached to the band with a rivet. The stone under the tallest point is green; the two on either side of it are red; and the two on the ends are blue. I place it on Mom's head, and she laughs as she comments, "I feel like a queen." I nod my head in agreement. Yes, she is the queen of my heart; and I am really her princess, not the Wishing Well Princess. That night, I fall asleep wearing the crown. It could never be more precious to me, even if it were made out of real gold and adorned with a real emerald, real rubies, and real sapphires. The doll, which I name "Grandy" after Granny and because she is so big, lies between Mom and me with her blue eyes staring up at the slanted ceiling.

The next day Tall Guy comes to visit. He has the photos he took of us some time ago. We crowd around to admire them. He gestures that we allowed to keep them. Mom offers him some change, which he graciously accepts. Then he takes more pictures of me with Grandy. Of course, I must wear the crown. He lifts me high into the air again—almost higher, it seems, than the big tree in our yard. Then he is off again to do some more visiting in town. After he leaves, I decided to take Grandy to the big rock with me. Smoky follows close behind. "Hi, this is Grandy," I announce holding her up for Big Brother to see.

"Pleased to meet you, Grandy," he replies. "I'm happy you have a new friend to take Granny's place, but don't forget that she will be back. I like your crown." As I reach up to touch it, I think about Granny. She would be so proud of me. I know Grandy can never replace her, nobody can. Then I remember why I came to visit Big Brother.

"You know Small Sis has a boyfriend. She claims she will marry him one day," I say, testing him for an answer.

Big Brother obliges by replying in his wise voice, "Believe it or not, she is right. One day, sooner than you think, she will marry White Knight. They will have five kids. The last two will be twin girls. The others will be one girl and two boys." I hold my breath thinking that my mom will be so pleased, but she would still not have a son of her own. "Stop feeling guilty," adds Big Brother as he reads my mind.

"I never thought Mom liked me until she told me she wanted, more than anything in the world, for me to be Wishing Well Princess," I confess.

"One day, before she dies, your mom will admit how much she loves you and your sisters. She will tell you how much she appreciates everything you have done for her over the years and how she wishes she would have had more daughters." All I can think about as I leave the rock is that some day my mom is going to die. In fact, we are all going to die. How could God be so cruel? I don't want any of us to turn into dust; I try to erase the dire thought from my mind.

Grandy becomes my special sleeping partner. Her wooden head, arms, and legs are covered with skin that will peel if I ever leave her out in the rain. When I need comfort, I cuddle her soft body. I often take her into the Main Street Bedroom, place the golden combs in my hair, and lie on Granny's bed with the doll close beside me. I can tell Grandy what I'm thinking, but she can't answer.

16

School is out for the summer. The house is almost always
full of girls, who are friends of my sisters; but boys are
beginning to hang around, too. When Med Sis and her
girlfriends happen to be lucky enough, they catch a ride
with some boy to a dance at one of the country halls on
Friday or Saturday nights. One morning, I am awakened
from a deep sleep by Mom's voice. She is whispering to
herself in Ukrainian, something to the effect, "Boy, is she
going to get it when she gets home!" She is referring to my
sister, who is apparently late getting home from a dance.
Mom is peering through the Main Street upstairs windows.
The sun is already starting to lighten the sky, and I hear a
rooster crowing in the distance.

She is about to speak again but is startled by Med Sis,
who raises her quilt above her head and moans, "What?" in
a sleepy voice. Mom obviously didn't hear her sneak in from
the dance only minutes earlier. She tries her best not to
laugh or show her embarrassment as she quickly leaves the
room. I hear the stairs creak as she makes her way down. I
know she is headed outside to work in her garden located
on the east side of our yard. She prefers to do her weeding
before the heat from the sun becomes unbearable.

My favorite pastime, of late, is hiding and listening to
my sisters and their girlfriends gossip about boys. While
they chat, they make cutouts—paper dolls that they draw
and color with pencil crayons, paste on light cardboard, and

then cut out. They design fashion clothing for the dolls, attaching the outfits to them with tabs on the shoulders and waists. I watch them and often copy their drawings. Once I drew a picture of a girl's face, which I framed with wavy hair. Then I added a shirt collar over a suit jacket collar. Med Sis was so impressed that she showed off my work to anyone who would take time to look and bragged about how good my drawing was for someone my age. They also sing songs and I learn the words. The girls always coax me to sing "I'm Sending You a Big Bouquet of Roses" because I use the words "pedals fall" instead of "petals fall" and then they snicker. I practice it along with many others singing to Smoky, who is my biggest fan, mainly, because I scratch him behind his floppy ears as I sing ever so loudly.

The upstairs bedroom is now littered with romance magazines, along with the cutouts. I sneak a peek at them when nobody is watching. I can't really read everything; but by looking at the pictures of guys and girls staring at each other or kissing, I know they imagine they are in "lo-o-ove" and yucky stuff like that. Whenever I am upstairs with the girls, I make sure to stay as far away from the troll's entrance as possible and am forever aware of it. They sprawl out on the beds for hours as they read and talk. One day, Med Sis tells her friends about a guy she was introduced to the night before. "Our eyes met across the smoky hall, and I knew we were meant for each other. He is tall with reddish-brown really curly hair and green eyes. Even though he seems shy, he asked me to dance. When he drove me home with his brother, one of the many songs he sang was, 'When Irish Eyes are Smiling'." I feel compelled to give Med Sis's love a name. In all of the stories Granny read to me, the girls have names like Snow White, Sleeping Beauty, and Cinderella. The girls, who read the books, can't be them because they already have their own names. Most of the boys in the stories aren't named and are kings, princes, knights, or warriors. I decide to name her guy "the Duke of Curl" because she has never seen such curly hair and because I heard of a Duke of Earl, but I can't remember where or when.

The next day, I am in the back yard playing with Grandy and Smoky. The golden combs are in my hair because I am desperately missing Granny. I notice Small Sis and a couple of her friends making several trips carrying bedding and boxes out of the back door and down the path past the big rock. Then they disappear behind the barn. When they don't return for some time, I decide it is safe to follow them but place my combs back into the box first. I stop at the rock on my way. I climb on with Grandy tucked under my arm and her long legs dangling down along one side of the rock. "Hi, Johnny," calls the familiar voice.

"Hello, again. I want to ask you something, but it has to be quick because I'm following my sister and I don't want her to hear us. Med Sis met this guy, and I want to know if love happens at first sight. Small Sis thinks she fell in love with her knight at first sight, too," I explain anxiously.

"Med Sis will marry Duke so I guess 'love at first sight' happens a lot," he replies supplying me with the answer I am expecting.

"Will they have any boy babies?" I want to know.

"Yes, they will have two and one girl," he answers. "But she will marry again later in life because her duke will not live as long as she does," he adds.

"I must go now," I sadly whisper thinking about the curly-haired duke with the green eyes as I slide off the rock. He is going to turn into dust before any of us. As I round the remains of the barn's old foundation, I hear voices and creep quietly through the bushes and trees toward the corner where two fences meet marking our property. I hide behind a small bush and find an opening from which spying on them is perfect. I watch Small Sis and her friends in their make-believe house. The branches of tall trees are intertwined with branches of shrubs to form a rounded ceiling; and the leaves on the bushes act as walls, thick enough for privacy. There are two smaller leafy rooms on either side of the main room whose ceiling of leaves is high enough to allow the girls stand up in it. The leafy house is strangely familiar to me—I have seen it before. I search my mind for the answer, and then it comes to me. Granny often spoke of a bower at her country home. She described it so vividly I felt I had been in it with her. Most of her summer days were spent lounging in her special chair under the leaves and ivy of her bower where she read her books and wrote. I just know this has to be a bower like Granny's.

I lean in closer to hear the girls' voices as they play house. Small Sis is the mom and one of the girls is the dad, White Knight. The shorter girl is their little boy. Two wooden pop cases placed one on top of the other serve as a table and four are used as chairs. The cupboards consist of stacked apple crates filled with old dishes and cutlery they probably found in the garbage heaps in the back alley. The bedding from upstairs is neatly arranged in the low, leafy bedrooms. I am trying my best to be quiet. Suddenly, in the blue of the sky above, I spot an aircraft and blurt out, "Air-o-plane, air-o-plane." The girls come running out to see it and are unaware, for the moment, that I am spying on them. We stand with our arms shielding our eyes and watch until it disappears into the clouds on the horizon. Such a sighting is rare for us. Then the girls turn to face me, and I know I am in trouble.

The little "girl-boy" shouts, "What are you doing here? You'd better get going..."

"You can stay but you have to be Johnny, our little boy;

and Grandy can be the baby girl," says my sister interrupting her and feeling sorry for me. Then she looks at her short friend and adds, "Now you can be the older girl."

"You must do the outdoor chores because, now, you are the boy," the girl says. "Here's a pail. Follow the path to the river and bring in the water to wash these clothes." I take the lard pail by its handle and head down the path. The pretend-river is really a ditch running along the road at the rear of our property. A plank runs across it. I am pleased to see for myself that there is not enough room for the troll to hide under the make-believe bridge. I feel safe as I balance on it and dip the pail into the water, skimming it along to avoid the black water beetles squirming around on top. Water sloshes over the rim as I shuffle back to the bower. My sister washes some old clothes and hangs them on the barbed wire fence. We have such fun pretending to eat meals, sleep, and do housework. Grandy seems to enjoy her shady room. Her eyes stare straight up, and she has a happy smile on her face. As darkness begins to fall, we pack everything into the boxes except for the bedding and cover the boxes with branches. We trudge back to the house carrying the bedding. I stuff a pillow under one arm and lug Grandy with the other.

Early the next morning, I arrive at the rock to speak to Big Brother. "I saw an air-o-plane yesterday so high up in the sky. I'd like to fly all over my country and over the ocean to where Jesus was born," I say remembering Granny's globe and the lesson that went with it.

"I can see you on an airplane flying in all directions over our country and also over the ocean. But beware! In the future, too many people will fly and live in countries where they weren't born. Flying will seem like a good thing because people will be able to travel wherever they want in a short amount of time, but all the movement from country to country and across the oceans will spread diseases. People become immune to diseases and insect bites in their own country, but diseases brought in from other countries can be deadly to large numbers of people. In the air, there will be terror; and on the ground, there will be hatred and violence because people of different races and different religions will discriminate against each other.

"People behave very much like animals or birds. Even chickens discriminate. If you have a flock of chickens of one type or color and you throw in one that is different, the others will peck at it until they kill it. One day, you will be surrounded by people of different races living in your neighborhood in the city. As for flying to where Jesus was born, Bethlehem will be a tourist attraction but will have to be shut down to visitors, even at Christmas, because there will be too much hatred for each other spewing over among 'the people of God.' They claim to worship the same God yet, unbelievably, don't think it's wrong to kill each other in the name of God. Military authorities will order a ban on landmines in an attempt to appear to care about human life and property but, at the same time, will allow soldiers to use weapons and drop bombs in order to kill and cause senseless destruction. Some males are, so to speak, born with a gun in their hand and are so used to carrying one they'd probably lose their balance and fall over if they ever put it down. The future Bethlehem will not 'lie still' as described in its Christmas carol and will be 'bright' from gunfire. Nations claim to want world peace, which could be possible if nobody showed up to fight."

I think about his wise words as I walk Smoky. Big Brother seems to be disgusted with our war and violence. I don't want to accept the fact that people of different religions and races are at war at this very moment and probably always will be. Even in our small town where residents are all Christians, I often detect the subtle animosity members of one church harbor towards members of another. I hate guns, war, and violence, too. My solution is that people who carry guns should only be able to shoot themselves, and I vow to never own one. My daddy would say, "Let live," with a long "i" as in "alive."

17

The end of summer is fast approaching. I spend most of my time at the playground or the bower, playing hopscotch in front of our store, and riding my tricycle. Daddy adjusted the seat and handlebars to the limit to accommodate my height. I dread the fact that I will soon outgrow it. On a Friday evening, the last one before school starts, I am watching a group of kids talking to my sisters in our yard under the big tree. A boy with dark hair and a scowl on his face hollers at me, "So, you're starting school on Monday. I know your teacher, and she's going to give you a strap at least three times a day." I flinch at the thought. If we were chickens, I'd peck at him. He is so mean looking. When he speaks in his nasty voice, his eyes narrow into thin slits. He laughs as he pushes some smaller kids around.

Another boy taunts, "Yeah! Are you going to get it! A strap three times a day! Ha, ha, ha!" That night and the following two nights, I toss and turn as I suffer through more troll nightmares. Now the troll holds a strap in his slimy hand similar to the one that hangs on the doorway between the kitchen and living room. It has three long wide leather strands, each with a leather circle on the end attached at the top to a ring, which is hooked on a nail too high up for me to reach. He has grown uglier than ever, and his red eyes gleam with glee as he swings the strap to make a snapping sound against his skinny knee.

I wake up in a sweat feeling scared and alone. It's Monday morning, my first day of school. I had decided what to wear long ago. Only Small Sis is rushing around getting ready. Med Sis wants to quit but must speak to the principal at recess today at the latter's request. I squirm into my pale yellow cotton dress with its fitted bodice, puffy sleeves, and skirt gathered at the waist and falling to my knees. Mom sewed it for me, and I love the heart pocket she stitched onto the skirt. I ask Small Sis to tie the two strands attached to each side of the waist into a bow at the back. We are ready to go, but I haven't eaten anything because I am too nervous. Mom is nowhere in sight. I follow Small Sis after she meets up with some friends. We climb the cement steps to the front entrance of the school. Then my sister gives me orders, "Sit at the top of the steps, and go into the school when you hear the bell ring." She disappears through the double doors as I look back. I sit there and pull my skirt down over my knees. Other beginners come up the steps with their mothers holding their hands. I am unable to curb the fear bubbling up within me and cringe when the bell rings. Instead of going into the school, I find myself running down the steps and down the road along the building sided with gray asphalt shingles. The principal, with the bell in her hand, is standing at the rear entrance calling me back. She is a tall, slender woman. Her hair is pulled back from a pretty face. The slightly flared skirt of her delicate lilac dress billows out softly in a gentle breeze.

She calls me again, "Come back, come back!" I decide that I have gone too far, and there is no turning back now. I run toward the path that cuts diagonally across a field in the direction of home. Tears sting my eyes as I stumble down the slippery side of a ditch and tumble forward. A feeble attempt to block my fall with my hands fails. When I manage to stand up, I am horrified to find my hands, knees, pretty dress, shoes, and socks covered with sticky mud. I continue to run down the path, across another ditch, over a road, over the plank crossing our ditch, and past the barn, big rock, toilet, and shacks to the back door, which is open. Med Sis spots me from inside the store.

"What happened to you?" she gasps as she stares at me in disbelief. "You're supposed to be in school."

"I ran away from school because I don't want to get a strap three times a day," I cry as I try to brush the mud from my dress with my dirty hands only making matters worse.

"That's not true. The teacher won't strap you. You're a good girl and smart. I'll take you with me when I go to see the principal at recess time. You'll have fun at school. You'll see. Don't worry. I'll take you," she consoles me as she helps me out of my muddy clothes and washes me off at the basin in the kitchen. I don't mind the stinging as she wipes off the scrapes on my hands and knees. I'm so happy that she seems to know exactly how I feel. While I change into my white dress with the red, orange, and yellow pansy design, my sister cleans off my shoes. She combs my hair into two French braids. I feel refreshed. When she is sure I am okay, she takes my hand as we confidently head for school.

"This is the Grade I room, and there is your teacher. Wait here while I talk to her," says Med Sis. She calls the teacher aside, and I watch them smile as they speak. I hope she isn't telling her that I expect to get a strap three times a day. Med Sis waves to me as she walks down the hallway, and the teacher approaches me. She is fairly tall and heavy-set. As I look up at her, I can't help but notice her huge breasts straining at the buttons of her white dress, which is covered with a floral pattern similar to mine. White buttons run all the way down the bodice and skirt of the dress. She is wearing white sandals. Her dark brown wavy hair is pulled back behind her ears with brown combs. She has a large mole on her cheek and some smaller ones on her neck. Her friendly smile reveals straight white teeth. Her dark brown eyes sparkle as she says, "Come, and we'll try to find somewhere for you to sit. All of the desks are taken."

The desk tables have seats attached to them. The only one left is the last one in the row near the back of the room. It has no seat so the teacher brings me a small wooden chair with a rounded back. Then noisy kids come barging in from recess break. The teacher takes control of her pupils and is soon handing out arithmetic workbooks. She instructs us on how to work on the first page. When I open the workbook, I am faced with outlines of shapes that need to be colored. The name of the shape and the color required is printed below each one. I color the square red and the triangle blue. Then I see the name of a color, "violet," under the rectangle. I don't know that one so I ask the teacher. "Oh, that is the same as purple," she explains. I like purple. The last shape is a circle and is to be colored pink. I have no pink so I color it red first and then with white as I have seen my sisters do. I stay in the lines. I don't want to get a strap. I have to be good because Mom doesn't need any more problems than she already has. The teacher comments on my wonderful coloring, and I feel my heart soar with pride. Then she reads us a story, and I am reminded of Granny. It's so good to have someone read to me again. Soon the bell rings, and I imagine the principal holding the bell on the back step of the school. The teacher informs us that we must go home for lunch. The problem now is that I don't want to leave. She assures us that we can come back when noon hour is over. I am the last first grader out the front door and take the same route home as I did earlier that morning, but I make sure to side-step the mud hole.

I run through the door singing, "I like school. I like school, and I didn't get a strap from the teacher yet." I find out that the principal has convinced Med Sis to finish her Grade XI. I am pleased, because Granny always reminded me about the importance of getting a good education and to finish high school, at least. I force myself to stay at home waiting for the noon hour to be over so I can go back. Then I play on the swings and teeter-totters in front of the school wishing the bell would ring. When it does, I am the first one into the classroom. The teacher hands out readers with a story about Dick, Jane, and Baby Sally. I study all of the pictures before she begins to read. Of course, Baby Sally happens to be wearing a white dress and matching white bow in her blonde curly hair. I ignore the picture and focus on the words. My favorite word in the whole book is a long one, "something," and it ends in my favorite letter, "g." I am tired and yawn repeatedly until we are dismissed from school at four o'clock in the afternoon. I take my time walking home down the diagonal path and stop at the rock to visit Big Brother. "Today was my first day of school, and I've decided to work hard and get good marks to please my mom and daddy," I vow.

"You'll do well, Johnny," replies Big Brother. "I can see you sitting in a university classroom, years from now, when you are much older, that is. Students are discussing with the professor the advantages of having had their fathers read them poetry when they were little—poetry from the likes of Tennyson, Wordsworth, and others. You'll smile to yourself and wonder what you are doing there because all your daddy ever taught you was how to play poker. I also see you in a photograph in which you are wearing a black graduation cap and gown. The gown has a white satin V-shaped band with a golden band underneath it, which is draped across your chest and around your shoulders. Your picture is framed between two other graduation photographs of persons who share your smile and eyes."

I head for home with Johnny's words again filling my head with thoughts of things to come. It has been a long day, this first day of school. As I am about to enter the living room, I happen to look up at the strap hanging on the doorframe.   I jump up high to give it a whack. Before the strap stops swinging back and forth, I am fast asleep on the sofa exhausted from the trials and tribulations of the day.

A couple of weeks into the school term, a new boy enrolls in my Grade I class. His tanned skin enhances the darkness of his black hair and eyes. For some reason, he takes a liking to me and chases me around at recess trying to kiss me. He owns what he claims is a "special" pencil. It is white and intertwined with shiny dark green grooves. His name is deeply engraved into the pencil near the eraser. "Boys are supposed to give girls presents," he says offering it to me. I like my regular gold pencil just fine and don't want his.

I blurt out an excuse for not accepting it, "It's a really nice pencil, but you're going to need it for class so you better keep it." Our conversation ends abruptly when the bell rings, and we hurry into the school.

The next morning, I discover the pencil on my desk. With its green lines shining menacingly, it resembles a snake basking in the light of the sun that filters through the window. I grab it and stick it in my desk just before the teacher enters the room. She is acting kind of strange and makes an announcement. "I want all of you to put your heads down on your desks and close your eyes. A student from a higher grade told me that his brother's pencil was stolen by someone in our classroom. It's white with shiny green lines and has his name carved on it." I feel sick to my stomach as she continues, "I want the person who took it to put it back on his desk." Nobody moves. After what seems like forever, the teacher commands, "Raise your heads." Then she begins to instruct the other two classes in the room. I stay behind after we are dismissed, retrieve the pencil, and drop it into his desk. From that moment on, I stay out of his way—boys are nothing but trouble. Much to my relief, days pass and the teacher does not again speak of the incident.

Med Sis signs up for a typing correspondence course and brings home a big typewriter, which she borrowed from the school. We all hang around the typewriter in the living room eager to take a turn. Finally, she orders us to leave her alone so that she can work on a budget, which consists of several sheets of drills to be typed according to instructions and sent out by mail for correction. Only one error per 8x5 sheet is allowed, and erasing is not permitted. One afternoon, after working on a budget for quite some time, Med Sis crumples up yet another sheet of newsprint and announces that she is going out to meet her friends. She knows I am itching to try the typewriter so she rolls in new paper and says, "You can try, but don't get the keys jammed. When you come to the end, just flip this lever and hold it while you push it back the other way." After a few more instructions, she disappears into the kitchen. The keys are all black so I look at the keyboard guide to find my favorite letter, G. I place my pinkie finger on the A. The others on S, D, and F, stretch my pointer finger to the G, and press hard. My fingers are too weak and, as a result, only a faint G appears on the sheet of newsprint. I am so excited because it is a fancy G just like the ones in my reader. I hit the key harder and harder until the G's are clear and dark enough to meet my satisfaction. I practice with my other hand and with both hands. I push down the shift key to make capital G's. I practice whenever the typewriter is free, and soon even my sister is impressed with my typing. She offers me five cents if I type a page for her budget. Finally, after many tries, I hand her a page that passes inspection and is sent out with hers. When the corrections come back, the marker comments that the typing on my page is uneven. However, it warrants a pass, which encourages me to practice more than my sister does. My typing improves, and I turn out more pages for budgets in the process.

18

Halloween is coming, and I decide to be an angel for the school party. I bug Mom and my sisters for days until they promise to make my costume. Mom sews me a floor-length dress with long wide sleeves out of fabric from an old sheet. When I try it on, I tie a piece of tinsel twine from the Christmas decorations around my waist. I look in the mirror and am pleased with the way it fits. My sisters make a halo out of flexible wire and twist some of the twine around it. They also make wings out of white cardboard and decorate them with twine. I ask them to make me a harp because I know that angels sit on clouds and play their musical instruments all day. They use the remainder of the wire, tinsel twine, and cardboard to create a fancy little harp that I can really strum. I have white stockings but no white shoes. Small Sis is certain there is a pair in the cubbyhole under the stairs. I crawl almost to the back of the dark storage area before I find them. They look pretty tiny, and we agree that they probably belonged to Frizzy at one time. I stuff the toes with tissues to keep them from flopping off my feet. My costume is complete, and I can hardly wait to wear it to the party. To add to my excitement, Daddy will be home in time for Halloween.

The first snowflakes of the season begin to fall as I head home at noon to dress for the party. Small Sis is there to help me with my halo and wings. I offered to bring cake to the party because almost everybody else was bringing sandwiches. There are several pieces of chocolate cake left over from Mom and Hattie's snack. Small Sis cuts them into smaller pieces, slides them onto a stiff piece of cardboard, covers them with wax paper, and slips them into a brown paper bag. I grab the package and head for school.

Everyone I meet admires my costume. Right after the bell , those who are wearing costumes parade past teachers who act as judges. I win a prize even though angels should really be blonde. I quickly open the package that is too small and flat to have Pumpkinhead inside of it. It's a box of crayons with my favorite colors, turquoise and magenta. After the parade, we play games including "Farmer in the Dell," "Fruit Basket Upset," and "Musical Chairs." Some of the boys keep tugging at my wings, which is pretty annoying. Lunch is served in time to distract them. I eat so many salmon sandwiches that I have no room left in my stomach for cake or cookies.

Everyone rushes home from school to don their costumes and prepare for an evening of fun. The days have become much shorter and the nights so much colder. Small Sis digs out a jacket for me to wear. It has white quilted lining so she turns it inside out to match my costume. I must leave the wings behind, but I am tired of them any way.

When it gets dark enough, we leave home and meet up with some of her friends. Then it begins to snow again.

My shoes are still too big, and I hobble along behind them hoping they would slow down. The faint glow of lanterns, which filters through windows, does little to help us see where we are going. It seems as though we are feeling our way through the darkness. When we come to a house, we yell, "Halloween apples," and that is what we get most of the time, just apples. Very few people hand out candy. We must cross a narrow bridge to reach the houses on the north side of town. I hope the troll doesn't come out on Halloween night and almost lose my balance twice, scaring me out of my wits.

By the time we get home, I am tired of the white shoes. The girls drop me off, empty their pillowcases, and continue on their way to the houses on the other side of the tracks. I look in my sack and take out all of the apples. Daddy helps me sort them. Most are bruised and a few are rotten. We dump out the candy, which I sample with both hands. Daddy keeps running outdoors every few minutes to check the toilet that was pushed over last year as a prank. He is determined to prevent the same thing from happening again. Noises coming from across the street attract our attention. We peer out the Main Street windows and spot movement in the shadows by the egg station. Daddy swears under his breath assuming that somebody is up to no good. He has a stick waiting by the door, grabs it, and goes running across the street. The perpetrators scatter in all directions. One figure disappears into the darkness running down Main Street toward the church with my daddy in hot pursuit. I worry about what might happen if he catches the culprit. I utter a long sigh of relief when he comes back swearing about the S.O.B. who escaped. Apparently, my dad interrupted the "Halloweeners" when they were stacking turkey crates on the egg station roof. Convinced that our toilet is no longer a target, I eat my candy on the loveseat and fall asleep there before my sister returns.

19

Health authorities predict that the time is ripe for another polio outbreak. All students must be vaccinated. I don't want to attend classes on needle day, but I do. Everyone is more concerned about how much the injection will hurt than about what the vaccine contains. Many of the kids cry, but I decide not to give those people the satisfaction of seeing me cry. I don't even flinch when the needle enters my arm. On the way home from school, I stop at the big rock. It is cold and icy, but I really want to speak to Big Brother so I climb on. "I was forced to get a needle today," I complain.

"An unidentified monkey virus has contaminated some of the polio vaccines and will be the cause of many diseases in the future, but you won't be one of those affected," he promises. "Doctors are also going to fill people up with drugs that will result in more health problems. One day, the use of many unsafe drugs will be questioned." I don't really understand what he is saying and imagine monkeys swinging on my ribs and other bones throughout my body. I hope I won't turn into a monkey one day. On the other hand, being a monkey might be fun. If I were a monkey, I'd be in a hot jungle right now eating bananas. Instead, here I am walking home through stiff grass covered with a skiff of snow and living in this freezing end-of-the-line place.

The school Christmas concert is to be held at the theater. I know Santa is invited because we practice singing "Here Comes Santa Claus". He is supposed to come in the door and run down the aisle as we sing. The day before the concert, I beg my mom to attend. Finally, she agrees. The next night, my sisters and I dress up in our white blouses and dark tunics after finding them in a bundle of clothes and having to press them with the iron that was on the stove and happened to be hot enough. However, we make it to the theater in plenty of time. All students are to sit on the benches in the front rows until the concert is over, and then the younger ones can join their parents after Santa comes.

The theater is beautifully decorated with red, green, and white streamers. A huge spruce tree, covered with colored lights and ornaments, stands tall to the left in front of the stage. Piles of gifts are stacked underneath it. I am anxious for Santa to bring me my Pumpkinhead. At the end of the concert, as we sing "Here Comes Santa Claus," he comes bounding down the aisle hollering, "Merry Christmas!"

After we finish the carol, I move to sit with my mom. As Santa calls out names, kids dash up onto the stage to receive their presents. Some get four or five big ones. When my turn comes, Santa hands me a small flat present that, definitely, does not contain Pumpkinhead. I open it with very little enthusiasm. My present is a set of paints in a green metal case, the same as the ones I saw at the store. I know it is from the gift exchange because I also bought a present for someone and put it under the tree. Santa has disappointed me again, and he is running out of chances. I don't get Pumpkinhead on Christmas morning either. I am glad he is jolly because I'm not, and I began to dislike him. I would certainly peck at him in his red suit if we were chickens. After Christmas, the weather becomes bitterly cold. Some days, when I am walking to school against the north wind, I fear that it will surely freeze my face off. I hate winter—it is for Santa Claus.

As time passes, I forget about Christmas and look forward to Valentine's Day. Med Sis helps me with my cards and envelopes. At the school party, one of the popular girls is crowned queen because she received the most valentine cards. The king is ugly, but he got more cards than the other boys did. The only good thing about the party is the large plate of salmon sandwiches but it is a flop compared to the Halloween party.

Daddy is home again for a long holiday. One night, shortly after his arrival, I awaken to loud voices and singing. I creep downstairs wondering what is going on. There are people partying and celebrating in the kitchen and living room. Everyone is speaking Ukrainian, but I know enough of the language to gather that Old Man Click got married. He holds his arm tightly around a little woman wearing a dark coat and large flowered kerchief folded just above her cheeks to cover her forehead and tied in a double knot under her chin. Every so often, he bends over to kiss her on her round nose. She blushes and gently swats him with her purse. He calls her by a name that sounds like "Petunia." I, myself, couldn't have picked a more perfect name for her because the flowered kerchief surrounds her face like the petals of a petunia surround its center. The happy couple sits close together on the sofa, and men keep filling the old groom's glass. When he has had enough to drink, he stands up to sing with Daddy. He sways back and forth and belts out his favorite song about a Baba's hole, a song I heard numerous times before. The other men laugh and the women appear embarrassed, but I don't know what the words mean. I fall asleep on the bed in Granny's room despite all of the commotion that lasts until the wee hours of the morning.

20

Spring has arrived and there is excitement in the air. Hydro is coming to town—electricity, that is! The work crew is to stay at our place, and Mom will also cook for the men. She is pleased with the arrangement, which gives her the opportunity to earn some much-needed money, and hires one of her relatives to help with the work. The men will be staying upstairs so we move our sleeping quarters back downstairs. The rear of the store is converted into an eating area for them. Mom also hires a carpenter to build a wall across the kitchen in line with the stairwell to replace the curtain, which separated that area from the kitchen and which now becomes my sisters' bedroom. We move the living room furniture into the Main Street Bedroom and Granny's bed into the living room to serve as a bedroom for Mom and me. Mom strings a curtain across the middle of the room to give us privacy because there is no door off the kitchen.

The heat from the cook stove is at times unbearable, so she does most of her baking in the early morning or late at night. My favorite item is her lemon pie. I can't wait to lick the lemon filling off the spoon and then the meringue from the beater. She uses plenty of eggs. One of my jobs, besides serving and helping clear dishes, is to run to the egg station for her. I enter quickly and close the door behind me making sure not to let out the cool air that always provides momentary relief from the heat outside. The egg man comes out of the dark area in the back, and I place my order, "A dozen cracks, please," as I hand him a dime. While I wait for him to return, I can never decide whether the building smells like cement or eggshells and wonder why it is always so cold in this place. He usually brings me the eggs in a paper bag or on a cardboard flat if they are badly cracked. After he opens the door for me, I slowly make my way across the gravel road being careful not to drop them.

Some of the hydro men work in the country installing poles and stringing wire, while others work in town wiring houses. Ours is one of the first places to be completed because the men are staying with us. They string wire throughout the house, but most of it is located in the troll's attic. Cheering erupts from all of us when Mom switches on the lights in the store for the first time! They are unbelievably bright and steady. I want to try. "Light on, light off," I chirp as I flip the switch up and down, and the lights flash on and off as if by magic.

"Don't do that too many times because the switch might break," somebody cautions.

One of the men takes a liking to me and calls me "Peewee." I reciprocate by nicknaming him "Frenchie" because he is French. His hair is so black it shines blue under the electric lights, and his mustache matches his hair. The reflection of my face appears in his wire-rimmed glasses whenever he holds me on his knee, and I notice that I always have a smile for him. Frenchie takes on Daddy's role in my life when my father is away at work. He often treats me to candy or gives me a couple of coins to spend. One of the guys develops an obvious crush on Med Sis, but she only has eyes for the Duke of Curl.

Now that all of the snow is definitely gone and the schoolyard is dry, practice begins for Field Day, which is our annual track meet. It is held at the playground behind

Mom's church. The rural schools, at least a dozen of them, participate in the meet along with ours. Their goal is to beat us at every event because ours is the big school. Besides track, there is a ball tournament and marching competition. Each school designs its own uniforms and banner. Our girls wear white blouses, red shorts, and white runners and socks while the boys wear white shirts, black pants, and black runners. We practice marching in the hot spring sun, day in and day out. The teachers are relentless, repeatedly calling out, "Left, left. Left, right, left."

Several students are chosen from each age group to participate in the tabloid, which consists of track and field events. I know I stand a good chance at being picked for throwing beanbags, running broad jump, and standing broad jump because of the skills I acquired from playing hopscotch. I am also a fairly good runner because I sprint a lot with Smoky and often run to and from school taking the back yard route. My wish to take part in the tabloid comes true. I am given the honor of representing my age group along with a couple of boys. However, my very favorite event is high jumping. I practice with Small Sis and her friends every day after school using the equipment that is left outside. Landing is difficult because the pit is filled with coarse gravel. The more we practice, the better landing becomes because the gavel is gradually displaced to the outer edges of the pit and only soft clay remains in the middle. I prefer to jump barefooted. At home, I set up a branch approximately waist-high supported by buckets and stones and practice for hours. I report to Frenchie about any progress I make. He always makes a big fuss about it and encourages me to keep on doing my best.

With all of the practicing and helping Mom with the chores and serving, my seventh birthday comes and goes without much notice. Besides, there are more exciting things about to happen than celebrating a birthday. Med Sis is to become a teacher! She will be attending "Normal School" in the big city for six weeks of teacher training, which begins the first week of July. I don't know how much more normal they can make her and decide I'll have to wait until she gets back to see if they change her.

Another event looming on the horizon is the visit of Big Sis, her husband, and two sons from out east. They will arrive some time in July and stay almost until the end of August. I must come up with a name for Big Sis's husband soon. Granny once read me a story about a Czar and his royal family so I decide to name him "Czar of the East," which sounds like the "Star of the East" in the hymn. Our Czar built a large model of a ship that often sails through the canal where they live and sold it to pay for their trip. Big Sis sent us a clipping from their local paper with a picture of Czar pointing out some interesting features on the model to their two boys—they were lucky to have had another son. While studying the picture, I name the dark-haired boy "Czar I" and the blonde one "Czar II." The model is very impressive with its intricate navigating equipment, portholes, and railings. I feel that the two boys will be a lot smarter and more important than I could ever be. The fact that boys are better than girls has been ingrained and reinforced in my brain since the day I was born. I am only halfheartedly looking forward to meeting them.

It has been raining for days so I thought Field Day would be cancelled; but it clears up, and the decision is made to go ahead with the event. The sun is shining again, but I shiver as I stand in the cool breeze in the lineup waiting for our turn to march. I feel the coarse gravel through my new runners as we march down Main Street— left, left... left, right, left! The grounds seem so far away. Once we arrive at the site, we are ordered to remain

standing at attention in our spots until the other schools
march in. The judges take their time deciding, but the results
are worth the wait. I jump up and down with the others
when they announce that our school takes first for best
marching; and we give our cheer, "Seesaw, ripsaw, buck
saw, BANG! We belong to the 'end-of-the-line' gang!"
I hold my breath as I throw the last of three beanbags, and it
hangs in the box just on top of the others. Our school needs
the points. Then, after many successful attempts in the high
jump competition, I run hard and spring up light as a
feather, clearing the bar, to win in my age group. After the
tabloid, in which our school places second, we join our
classmates for lunch. We sit in a circle with women handing
out food from baskets and serving containers in the center.
Trees line the perimeter of the grounds, but there are none
to provide shade where it is needed. The sun beats down on
us, and some of the kids are already showing signs of
sunburn. One of the women fills my paper cup with a red
liquid that sparkles in the sunlight as she pours. I drink it
slowly allowing it to trickle down my parched throat. Then I
reach for sandwich after sandwich every time the basket is
passed around. The bread is fresh and cool, and I eat every
bit of it. I notice with disgust that some kids discard their
crusts. For dessert, the women serve triangles of
watermelon, which I taste for the first time. Then the boys
start a watermelon pit fight that almost escalates into a riot,
and the women drag them apart by their collars.

In the long race, my heart pounds in my chest harder
than my feet on the grass as I try to catch up to the girl
ahead of me. I can see her flowing blonde hair from the
corner of my eye as I draw on a burst of energy and sprint
past her just before the finish line. By the end of the day, I
have three red ribbons pinned to my blouse across my chest.
I also have a blue ribbon, a second, from the three-legged

race in which I almost had to carry my partner. The winners tied their nylon stocking around their ankles so loosely that it fell off before they reached the finish line. I also win a white ribbon, a third, for the wheelbarrow race. I should have been the wheelbarrow because my partner's arms weren't strong enough to keep her up, even though I practically carried her too. Back at home, Frenchie admires all of my ribbons and smiles as he pats my head. "I sure am proud of you, Peewee. I saw you win the race. I snuck away at coffee break for a few minutes to watch you," he chuckles in his special way. He is always ready with words of praise for me and seems to know how to make me feel special. Then he digs in his worn leather wallet and pulls out a dollar bill that he places in my hand and closes my fingers over it with his.

"Frenchie, it's too much," I gulp, but he insists I keep it. Then he joins the other workers for supper. I decide to rest on the sofa for a few minutes and end up falling asleep without taking off my runners, shorts, or the blouse with the ribbons attached to it. Frenchie's dollar is still crumpled up in my hand where he placed it when I wake up the next morning.

Everyone is excited about the school year coming to an end but nervous about writing exams. I have exams, too. On the last day of school, I am afraid to look at my report card but decide it is a good one after mustering up the courage to examine it. As I am leaving the building, one of the teachers approaches me. I hope I have not done anything wrong. To my surprise, he offers me six beanbags to take home for the summer. He noticed my practicing, even after Field Day. I skip happily all the way home down the diagonal path carrying the beanbags and checking my pocket every so often to feel my report card. I don't get the praise I am longing for from Mom as she signs it. I place it in the box with Granny's combs for safekeeping until school starts again in the fall. In the box is Frenchie's dollar. Tears come to my eyes because I know he will be leaving tomorrow. His job here is finished.

After work the next day, Frenchie hangs a Christmas orange crate underneath the fire escape at the back of the store so I can practice throwing bean bags in the shade all summer. We take turns tossing. He is very good and gives me some pointers. "Concentrate, and keep your eye on the box," he urges. I follow his instructions, and my next three bags land in middle of the box. "Peewee, I'm sorry I have to leave," he says as he reaches into his jacket and pulls out a box wrapped in yellow paper. He doesn't know about Pumpkinhead. If he did, he would be the one to get him for me. I open the parcel with trembling hands. Inside the box is a blue owl wearing a graduation cap.

"I'm going to wear one of those one day, Frenchie," I whisper making the promise, not only to him but also to myself, as I recall Big Brother's prediction.

"I'm sure you will, Peewee," he agrees with a grin. "I hope you do attend university one day. If you work as hard there as you did for Field Day, you'll have no problem graduating. Here's some money for the owl. It's a bank. Drop the coin into the slot in the top of its hat." I notice that the owl's eyes are tightly shut. When I drop a quarter into the slot, its golden eyes blink wide open as the coin disappears. Frenchie hands me dimes and pennies, which I continue to feed into the owl's cap. Some of his co-workers gather around us to watch. Frenchie asks them for coins for the owl, but they don't want to give me any.

"You cheapskates," hollers Frenchie as they scatter. "Now I want you to think of me whenever you put money in; and when the owl blinks, you'll know that I am thinking of you," he adds softly. Then he kneels down and gives me a hug.

"Thank you so much for the owl, Frenchie. I just love it," I reply. As he turns to leave, I hold the owl close and run to the bedroom crying, "Why do people I love always have to leave?" I dream about the troll again.

In the morning, Frenchie is gone.

21

After watching Med Sis trying to stuff all of her belongings for Normal School into two small suitcases, I run to my cot and drag out Frizzy's suitcase. "You can borrow mine," I say offering it to her.

"Brilliant!" she exclaims as she sets it on the bed. "Now I can pack everything I need and take my small suitcase, too. If I want to buy something in the city, I will have room to bring it home." I sit on the bed with my feet dangling above the floor and balancing my shoes on my toes while I watch her fill the suitcase. I ask her questions about what she would do there at Normal School, but she isn't quite sure herself. I know I will really miss her and wonder how I will survive without Frenchie and her until our visitors arrive from out east.

Monday morning comes. I am dreading the moment when my sister must leave. She is doing some last minute packing and keeps fussing with her hair. As she looks in the mirror, she puckers her lips and applies some red lipstick. Stepping back, she asks, "Can you run to the store for one of those brown boxes?" I wrinkle up my nose. Before I can make up an excuse, she adds, "I'll give you five cents if you go for me. Please, pretty please," she whines making me laugh.

"Okay, I'll go," I agree halfheartedly. She writes a note for me to give to the Man with the Long Fingernail. When I return with the box, she stuffs it into the corner of Frizzy's suitcase and snaps the lid shut. Then we carry her luggage downstairs and wait for a friend who is to room with her at Normal School. Mom joins us seconds before a blue car pulls up. The friend's mom is driving them to the big city. My sister places her suitcases in the trunk and jumps into the car. She smiles at us and waves as the car makes a U-turn. I wave, just a little wave, and hold back tears. We watch until the car rounds the corner and disappears behind the church.

I spend most of the afternoon tossing beanbags into Frenchie's crate and bouncing my sponge ball against the back wall of the store. My ball is half red and half blue with a white ring around the middle. I also invent a new game for myself. Looping two rubber rings to form a knot in the middle, I stretch one loop over my left thumb, which I use for aiming at the little window in the staircase, and pull the rings back with the pointer finger of my right hand to let them fly. After some practice, I am able to shoot the rings through the window. I make five of the double-looped rings. After shooting all of them through the window, I run up the stairs and shoot them back down. I play my game for hours. Besides practicing my typing, hopscotch, and high jumping, I ride my tricycle around outside and bring it in later in the evenings to ride around the table in the store. I am a busy girl and beginning to enjoy being alone. The days are becoming longer, and we have hydro so everyone stays up later. Nobody tells me when it is time to go to bed or to get up.

In winters past, before the Hydro came, farmers and

fishermen would come into town with their horse-drawn cabooses. The little canvas or wooden huts built on sleighs were equipped with wood-burning heaters inside to keep the driver and passengers warm. They lined the streets with smoke curling up from the pipes sticking out of the roofs on cold frosty days. With the arrival of hydro, our town enters a boom. Stores stay open until eleven o'clock on Friday and Saturday nights. Many of the farmers now own trucks and cars, which they park diagonally on both sides of Main Street. Teens take in the movie or hang around at the cafes on the weekends while their parents congregate in the stores to chat, visit, and stock up on groceries and farm supplies. We have company galore.

When I walk home from the theater after the weekly movie, I must now be careful crossing Main Street because the traffic in front of the hotel is the busiest with vehicles constantly pulling in and backing out of parking spots. They even park in front of our place. Only men are allowed in the hotel, which includes the Indians from the reservations north of town. Women and children have to wait in the vehicles until the men come staggering out at closing time, hours after the stores close. Almost every weekend there is a fight, with the Indians being the main participants. Sometimes I watch with my mom as we hide in the shadows where we won't be seen. The Indians box with their fists, tear at each other's clothes until they are in sheds, and roll around in the gravel and mud in the lane until they are dirty and bloody. They curse at each other all the while. We stand so close to them that we can hear the thuds from the blows they throw and their heavy breathing as they are sapped of strength. Their women scream and cry and often attempt to physically break them up. Finally, when the men are worn out, they stumble to their vehicles for a rest. Then they throw in their cases of beer and speed away with gravel flying, leaving the town in silence. They always come back the next weekend for more.

I hate the violence and swear to myself that I will never drink. The moaning of the women and children rings in my ears as I toss and turn trying to fall asleep after witnessing a fight. A constant threat is that those drunks might someday find their way into our home. Time after time, I hook the front door while squatting behind the screen just as one of them tries to open the door from the other side. My heart pounds with fear causing my hands to shake so badly that I can hardly slip the hook into little loop to secure the door. Mom often leaves the doors open so I take it upon myself to make sure they are locked every night before going to bed.

To my surprise, Mom buys some chickens and ducks from a farmer. I help her fence off a large area with chicken wire to enclose a wooden shelter and a pond for the birds between the shed and my rock. The shallow pond fills up with water whenever it rains. I enjoy sitting with my back resting against the south side of the rock to watch the hens scratch and peck at the ground while the ducks waddle around or swim in the pond scooping up bugs with their beaks and flicking water onto their backs. Now we have our own eggs to eat. We don't butcher the birds because they quickly become our pets.

Med Sis promised to write me a letter from Normal School so I check our mailbox at the post office every day. I stand on my tiptoes to open it with the key and then slide my hand in and feel around because I am too short to see inside. No letter comes so I decide to write to her first. The letter, which I print all by myself with pencil on newsprint, begins as follows: When are you going to send my 5 cents?

22

Big Sis and her family will be arriving the last week in July, in time for the fair in August. They plan to stay until the end of the month in order to visit with Med Sis for a couple of weeks after she returns from Normal School. I am now anxious to meet the Czars. The Saturday before their arrival is an unfortunate one for me because Mom decides to cut my hair. It had grown past my shoulders, and I liked it long. Hattie's brown hands hold me down while I kick and squirm trying to save my hair by pushing away at the scissors in Mom's hand as she cuts. With every snip, I feel my precious hair fluttering to the floor all around me. When it is over, I stare at myself in the mirror with eyes that are red and swollen from crying. My hair is cut straight around just below my ears. I hate it, but Mom insists that if I want long hair in the future I will have to care for it myself. I take out Granny's combs and pull the hair away from my face clipping it in place. I still don't like it. As I lie on the bed, I wish Mom would have left my hair alone, at least until the Czars went home. I dream about the troll again and wake up in the morning feeling scared and alone.

The day Mom expects the Czars, she anxiously glances out the Main Street windows in the store, every so often, praying for them to have a safe journey. Darkness falls, and there is still no sign of their vehicle. Around midnight, Smoky begins barking excitedly emitting sharp yelping noises. When a face appears in the window of the back door, he jumps, time after time, almost as high as the ceiling. He recognizes his first master, probably by scent. When Mom opens the door, Smoky, with his stubby tail wagging in a blur, is the first to greet the Czar of the East. Her son-in-law pats Smoky all over his body, and the dog begins to calm down as Big Sis appears cradling one of her sleeping sons in her arms. I identify him from pictures as being Czar II. His dad takes him upstairs, goes out again, returns with Czar I, and carries him up, too. While Mom and her daughter hug and talk, he hauls several pieces of bulky luggage up the stairs. I am tired so I crawl into bed and listen to their voices, which drone on for most of the night.

I am up early the next morning and run outdoors to inspect their car. It is light green in color, decorated with shiny chrome, and sits on Main Street like a large water beetle resting after a long swim. As I peer inside the passenger window, I wish that I can have a ride in it one day. I return to the kitchen and stand near the back door, out of the way, when the family comes downstairs. Big Sis has medium blonde hair and is wearing a white blouse and pedal pushers. Her husband has black hair combed back from a receding hairline. Dark-rimmed trifocals sit on his broad nose. He wears a cotton shirt and dark pants. The boys, dressed in matching red, white, and blue striped T-shirts with tan shorts, cling to their mother. Their hair cut so short that I can see their scalps. Czar II is wearing saddle shoes like his mom—white shoes with a wide dark band resembling a saddle straddling the top and sides of the shoe. His brother is wearing dark loafers that tie in the front. The boys look strangely ordinary, which is not what I was expecting. I keep my distance and don't participate in the conversation.

Later that morning, when I walk into the kitchen, Czar II is sitting in a tub of water on the kitchen table. My sister is soaping him down. As I join them to watch him have a bath, my eyes are drawn to something between his legs near his body. At first, I think it's a toy. When I look more closely, I see that it is attached to him. It looks like a short, fat earthworm extending into flesh covered balls that are also attached to his body. I am shocked when I discover, at that very moment, what really makes boys and girls different. I am disgusted with the purpose of that difference and must get out of the room now. As I dash out the door, everything falls into place. Discussions I overheard about the birds and the bees, dinks and balls, and girls and guys sleeping together make sense now—guys are sticking their dinks into the girls, that's how babies start. That is why they say girls in Grade IX or X leave school—they "have" to get married. I even know what's in those brown paper-covered boxes at the store—pads for when girls have their "periods." I know now that I can never be a boy and am angry with myself for being stupid enough to think so. I wouldn't want to be one anyway and have an ugly thing like that. My eyes are stinging with tears by the time I reach the big rock. I beat at it with my fists as I scramble on. Through clenched teeth, I barely manage to spit out my words. "Big Brother, I know you're here." I feel his presence but I don't give him a chance to answer. "I just saw an earthworm dink. I don't want to be Johnny any more. I want you to be Johnny. I'm glad I'm a girl. I don't think I could ever get close enough to a boy to have kids. I hate boys, even more now. I don't know why they are so special to everybody."

"Shush, it's okay," he whispers trying to comfort me. "I'll be Johnny from now on if you want me to be. I can understand what you are feeling now, but you will be a mother one day. I can see you, as a young woman, looking out a window decorated with ruffled curtains. You are watching two children at play. One is sitting on a swing.

The sun is shining brightly causing a shadow from the child's eyelashes to form on its cheek. Nearby stands a younger child holding a small animal in cupped hands. The animal is alive. It's a pet… "

I interrupt Big Brother mumbling, "I don't want to hear any more… I don't want to hear anymore." I am overcome with exhaustion when I leave the rock. Instead of heading for home, I turn in the opposite direction allowing myself to be drawn to the bower where I can take refuge. I don't want to face anyone now, especially, the Czars. Once inside, I drag a blanket out of one of the apple crates, roll it up under my head, curl into a tight ball under the low-lying branches, and wait for sleep to come. When I wake up, I feel better but experience the need to keep my mind blank, not daring to think about the knowledge revealed to me earlier in the morning. As soon as I crawl out of the bower, I begin a search for straight branches or trees suitable for constructing my own high jump equipment. I discover two for posts and a reasonably long one for a bar. After stripping off branches, I drag them past the barn, the rock, and the bird pen. I set them down in front of the small shack where the ground is flat and the area is large enough to make a running approach. With luck, I find some nails with huge heads and long enough to hold the bar in place and Daddy's hammer. I begin pounding nails into the makeshift poles that lie on the ground at the heights I estimate I can easily jump and then higher for a challenge.

Czar I comes out the back door and observes me from a distance. As he creeps closer, I watch him from the corner of my eye. He has a handful of metal bottle caps—the kind with crimped edges to fit securely on pop or beer bottles, and probably found them in the garbage heap behind the outhouse. As I work, he begins to flick them at me. They sting my leg and arm, but I choose to ignore them until one strikes me above my eye. "Stop it," I snap, "you can hurt my eye." I grab the first thing I see, which is a small flashlight battery lying with some junk in front of the shack. "If you throw one more, I'm letting you have it!" I warn. He flicks one more, two more. I duck to protect my face. As I quickly lunge forward, the battery accidentally rolls off my hand. It barely hits him on his shoe below his ankle, but he scampers into the house screaming. I follow close behind to explain what happened. I know I didn't hurt him. By the time I get to the kitchen, Mom has the strap in her hand catching me by surprise as she swings it across my bare legs. She swings it hard, again and again. I feel the welts rising on my flesh. As I scramble out the back door, I can hear Big Sis chasing her son up the stairs hollering at him. I head for the bower and huddle under the branches whimpering quietly. Feeling sorry for myself, I vow to stay away from boys from now on. When I muster up enough courage to sneak back into the house, it is getting dark. As I crawl into bed, my thoughts focus on the troll. I won't let him control my dreams, not tonight. I force myself to judge him and scorn him. I'll bet he has a green earthworm dink. He makes me sick. I hate him as much as I hate all boys. They are nothing but trouble.

When I open my eyes, the sun is coming up. My body feels stiff and sore and my legs are scraped, bruised, and burning. I am thankful that Mom is nowhere to be seen because I have a plan. Using the fly swatter, I knock the strap off its nail on the doorway. I grab it as it falls and hold it out in front of me as I open the small cubbyhole door under the stairs where shoes and boots are stored. Flinging it as far as I can, I am confident that nobody will find or use it ever again. Successfully managing to avoid everyone, I escape back to the bower. Small Sis, who is feeling sorry for me, finds me later in the afternoon and brings me a slice of bread and jam. She helps me erect my high jump apparatus, and I spend the next several days running, jumping, and keeping to myself.

23

Oh, happy day! The fair is coming to town! Big trucks roll into the grounds behind Mom's church. The workers set up the two rides, a Ferris wheel and a merry-go-round swing, and food and game booths for the one-day event. Early the next morning, crowded cars and trucks loaded with people standing in their boxes begin arriving for the celebration. Mom definitely isn't going to the fair. She never goes anywhere except to church or to visit my aunts. Big Sis plans to attend the fair with her family, and Small Sis is meeting her friends at the grounds. They are all dressed up and decide that a photograph of the whole family should be taken when Tall Guy shows up. Everyone lines up on Main Street; and Mom, who is holding Czar II, grabs me by the arm pulling me towards her. I don't want to stand anywhere near Czar I. My hair is ugly, and I don't want a picture taken of it. I feel uncomfortable, as though I don't belong there, but Tall Guy takes the picture anyway.

For weeks, even months, I have been saving money I found on the street in front of the beer parlor or in between the sofa and armchair cushions in the living room. Praise the Lord for the hydro men, who lost quite a few coins that are now in the box with Frenchie's dollar! If it weren't for them, I wouldn't have enough for admission and rides. After everyone leaves and I see that Mom is busy, I hurry off by myself. Crowds of people are milling about town, so nobody takes any notice of me. I meet up with some kids from school who invite me to sneak into the grounds with them on the path running under the fence near Mom's church. Making up an excuse, I tell them I have something to do first. I don't want to join them and get caught as I have been in too much trouble of late. Instead, I pay my admission at the gate and receive a stamp on my hand. I immediately walk over to the Ferris wheel and try to imagine what it would be like to stop at the very top. The operator is a young fellow wearing a T-shirt with the sleeves torn off. "Don't be shy," he hollers. "Just step up, and I'll give you a long ride." I hand him my money, and he lets me stay on for almost half an hour. Each time, going down, my stomach feels the same as it does when I jump out of the attic. He makes me stop at the very top several times. I am so high up in the sky I can see our place over the trees. Later, the man running the swings lets me on for free to balance the ride. The ride makes me dizzy, and I feel sick to my stomach. What makes matters worse for me is that the heat from the sun is becoming unbearable, and there isn't much shade. I don't want to watch baseball so I decided to walk around the booths and rides once more before going home. I see Big Sis and her family so I duck behind a tent, which proves to be a stroke of luck. On the ground, I find a little doll. I pick her up and straighten out the dints on her face and body. A pink feather sticks out of her head and more form a skirt around her stomach. I am disappointed in the fair but must admit that the Ferris wheel ride was special. Smoky is happy to see me. After playing with my new doll for a while, I place her next to Frenchie's owl, which is now empty of coins, under my bed.

The day of Med Sis' return from Normal School finally

comes. She is so excited about being home, visiting with Big Sis and the Czars, that she has little time for me. I keep to myself, realizing that I am becoming an expert at being alone.

On the last Sunday of the Czars' visit, some of my aunt's relatives from out west come over in the afternoon. They have three young sons who are wild and mean. One of them is wearing hard-toed black shoes and kicks me every chance he gets. The Czars are riding my tricycle, and the other three boys pile on. I run to tell my mom that the boys are too heavy and are going to break my tricycle, but she is busy visiting with everyone and just says, "Oh, let them play." By the time I get back, one of the rear wheels has been broken off my beloved trike. The boys all scatter. Tears come to my eyes as I inspect the damage. It appears to be beyond repair because everything is bent. I drag it under the counter and sit with it sobbing all the while. My mourning is interrupted by a ruckus coming from the boys in the back yard. I run out to see what is causing the commotion. They are chasing one of the young ducks, which has escaped from the pen. The boy with the hard-toed shoes corners it and kicks it once, twice, three times in the breast. I holler at him to stop but he doesn't listen. By the time I able to rescue the duck, it is too late. Its legs are stretched straight out, and I can see the webbing between its toes. The duck's eyes close slowly as I gently stroke its feathers realizing it is dead. I face the boy with the hard-toed shoes. I know he has an earthworm, too, and that makes me madder.

"Look at what you did. The next time you kick me or anything else with those hard-toed shoes I'll kick you right back," I threaten. I know I could give him a boot and get away with it without getting another lickin' because of the whereabouts of the strap. His parents happen to come out, at that moment, saving him from my wrath. I am so happy to see him leave with his family that I never want to see any of them ever again.

Later that evening, Small Sis, her friends, and I have a funeral for the duck. We dig a hole in the dirt by the rock. The duck looks so small and innocent in the bottom of the cardboard box with its body sprinkled with buttercups. Parading around the rock, I carry the makeshift coffin while we chant, "Hos poh deh poh meh loi, hos pod deh poh meh loi", over and over again just like they do in Mom's church. Then we recite "The Lord's Prayer" as we lower the coffin into the grave. Everyone leaves after the burial, but I stay behind needing to speak to my brother.

"Johnny, where are you? Those boys broke my tricycle and killed my duck," I sputter waiting for his answer that better be good.

"I know. I'm so sorry for you and so embarrassed for them. One day you'll find a way to ride your trike again. New ducklings will hatch in the spring," consoles Johnny in an attempt to reassure me.

"But that doesn't make what they did right, and their parents didn't even care. If I did that to those precious boys, I would have got a lickin'. I just don't understand," I moan.

"Most parents think their sons can do no wrong," agrees Johnny. "There is an old Chinese proverb that goes something like this: A man would rather have a deformed, mentally retarded son than a perfect, clever daughter." I don't want to believe it; but in the back of my mind, I know it is true. I trudge back to the house feeling depressed and wondering what Johnny meant when he said that I would ride my tricycle again.

Next morning, everything is packed into the Czars' car, and they are homeward bound. It is a sad day; I experience mixed feelings about their leaving because I never patched things up with Czar I after the bottle cap incident.

24

We are all excited about the fact that Med Sis landed a teaching position at a country school seven miles away. Only one weekend remained before the beginning of school when she asked me if I would like to live with her at her teacherage and have her for my Grade II teacher. She didn't ask me sooner because she just received permission from the supervisor to allow me to attend the school. Mom leaves the decision up to me. I gather together my clothes, a few dolls, and my special keepsakes and pack them into Frizzy's suitcase, which Med Sis mptied after returning from Normal School. The following evening, the Duke of Curl drives us to the teacherage. He has a gray car also shaped like a water beetle. Music is playing on the radio as he drives along the straight and narrow country road, steering with one hand while holding a cigarette in the other. I sit in the back behind him and notice how curly his hair really is. It is even curly where his neck is shaved. We make a left turn, and he announces we have a mile left to go. Then we pass a church with a small cemetery. As we enter the schoolyard, I anxiously survey the school and "the teacherage" that will be my home for the entire term. The school is small with gray asphalt shingle siding and windows along the east side. The teacherage is located scarcely a stone's throw away. It is a square building, approximately the size of four double-holed toilets, with white siding and a single-pieced black roof that slopes slightly from the front to the back of it.

A window on the side faces the school. Two outhouses, boys and girls, are located to the south so as to form a triangle with the school and teacherage. The yard is fenced with barbwire in front of the dense bush to the east side of the teacherage and behind the toilets.

Duke parks in front of the teacherage. Then my sister climbs the two steps and opens the teacherage door with a skeleton key. Duke stands beside her, and I curiously peer in after them. Then I squirm in ahead of them eager to see the place. In the middle of the main area, which serves as a kitchen and living room, sits a potbellied stove. I flip aside a faded yellow curtain covering the front of a cupboard to find it contains pots, pans, and a kettle. A small wooden table with a coal oil lamp perched in the center and surrounded by three matching chairs takes up the space under the window facing the school. My sister opens a trap door in the floor in front of the stove to reveal a shallow cold storage area dug into the dirt. The other room is the bedroom, which contains a double bed, small closet, and apple crates that serve as a dresser covered with the same fabric as the kitchen curtains. A mirror with a wide carved frame hangs above the dresser. I immediately feel safe and at home in the tiny house mainly because it has no hiding place large enough for the troll.

We walk across the dry grass to inspect the school. Its entrance serves as a cloakroom with hooks along one wall. The classroom is large with a wood-burning heater at the back. Duke carries in a couple of boxes filled with books, folders, and papers and places them on the teacher's desk while my sister practices ringing the cowbell. Then we head back to the teacherage and help Duke carry in our supplies and suitcases. We unpack everything in a hurry filling up the cupboard with canned goods, the cellar with dairy products, and the closet and apple crates with our clothes.

Everything must be sorted out before dark because the teacherage has no electricity. When we are finished, my sister lights a candle on the table. I disappear into the bedroom to give them some privacy because I know they are in "lo-o-o-ove." The mattress feels firm and lumpy against my body. After I lie there watching the dancing shadows on the walls and ceiling formed by the flame of the flickering candle for a few minutes, I doze off. My sleep is briefly interrupted when Duke's car leaves, and Med Sis crawls into bed beside me.

The ringing of bells seemingly just above our heads awakens us. The sound is coming from the church summoning farmers to the Sunday service. Instead of attending church, we each grab a slice of bread and jam and head for the school. I snoop around while Med Sis unpacks her boxes and prepares her class lists and lessons. I find library books and art supplies on the shelves in the back of the room but am happier with the beanbags and high jump equipment, which are stored in a tall closet in the cloak-room. The poles are so light I am able to set them up myself. Before I know it, I am back into my old routine of tossing beanbags and high jumping. Then I discover a balance beam constructed of rough posts anchored into a clearing near the fence. After a few botched attempts, I am able to run up, across, and down with ease. I vow to never venture into the bush because it harbors a small cemetery.

Soon Med Sis is ringing the bell for real, signaling the beginning of a school year for her new students, including me. In all, she has seventeen enrolled in classes from Grade I to VIII with nobody in Grade III. I am in Grade II with two boys. One sits ahead of me and the other behind me.

Health inspection is required by the school board and is the first topic discussed after singing "O Canada." Med Sis lists the rules on the blackboard, explains what is expected of us, and tells us to copy the rules into our notebooks. While still in the process, I decide my scribbling does not at all resemble what she has written on the board and panic. Would I ever learn to write properly or fulfill the requirements of health inspection? Every morning she is to check our necks, ears, hands, and fingernails to make sure they are clean. We each must produce a clean handkerchief on her command. Those not meeting the standards receive an "X" on the chart next to their name. Houses on the farms and the teacherage have no sinks, bathtubs, running water, or electricity. The farms have wells or dugouts but water must be heated on stoves. Water for the school and teacherage is hauled in from the nearest farm and carried in with pails by one of the students. Some of the families are large. How could they meet the standards of health inspection decided upon by authorities living in the larger centers who enjoy the luxuries of running water, electricity, and bathrooms? It just doesn't make sense to me.

Our first handwriting lesson focuses on the alphabet, "a." We practice making horizontal spirals on our ruled pages first, then rows of the small and capital "a's," and then words beginning with "a." I have been working on spirals since my health inspection scare—stationary spirals, spirals which gradually decrease, and those which gradually increase. As a result, my "a's" come out perfectly formed. Med Sis is impressed. She doesn't comment about in class but praises me later when we are eating supper, and I beam in response.

Days pass quickly. We usually hitch a ride into town with one of the farmers for the weekend and catch a ride back with Duke. Then Med Sis invests most of her first paycheck on a vehicle. I am so overcome with joy when she drives the car home and parks it in front of our place that I jump up and down. My sister is so special—in my eyes, she can do anything. She is making history in our town. Until this moment, I have known of only guys owning cars. Hers is the most beautiful water beetle car I have ever seen. I cheer when she leans over, opens the passenger door for me, and announces, "I'm treating you to a ride to the Three-Mile Corner." I stand up in front of my seat in order to see out the windshield. As she jerks the clutch, I hang onto the dash for balance. We quickly round the corner and whiz past the church with dust rising behind us.

"Now we're making dust instead of eating it," I holler with excitement as I glance back to see the plume of dust following us. Our mood changes as we nervously watch a vehicle approaching ours in the distance. The road is narrow so she decides to stop on the side before meeting the other car. Then she starts up again, drives past the cemetery, and turns around at the Three-Mile Corner. By the time we return home, she meets two cars without stopping. Whenever she drives to the teacherage, I stand looking out over the dash, never missing a rut in the road or a branch of a tree. We even make a long trip into the big town with the car. I stand in the front, as usual, for over an hour. Med Sis has an appointment with the optometrist. She knows she needs glasses. I want glasses to be like her and tell the optometrist that I can't see the blackboard and that the sun makes my eyes water. A few weeks later, we receive our glasses in the mail. She wears hers all of the time, but I wear mine only occasionally.

When we come home from the teacherage one weekend in October, we discover that a radio repairman has set up his shop in the back of the store. I watch him closely as he works. Within hours, I am able to make a reasonable diagnosis of what is wrong with a radio by the sound it makes. Weak reception means it needs a new tube. When a radio makes a screeching noise, I know it needs a new condenser. He removes the condenser by heating up the solder around the wires and then solders in a new one. I like the smell of it. Whenever I am at home, I proudly sit on his workbench with my feet dangling high above the floor waiting for him to consult with me about radios dropped off by his many customers.

Med Sis's next major purchase is a wind-up gramophone and some 78 records. Small Sis or one of her friends is usually her dance partner, but the radio repairman is always mine. I name him "Jigger-r-r-r-ram" because he likes to jig. In the middle of working on a radio, he often stops to dance to the music coming from his own, which he keeps on at all times. He is not very tall with a slim build and hooked nose. Small Sis often comments about his excessive use of styling cream. Streaks of it are visible in his dark hair that is slicked back from a receding hairline. When we dance, we clasp hands and make two small hops to one side and then to the other. Around and around the display table we go keeping time to the beat of polkas like "Maple Syrup" and "Roll out the Barrel." We even make a polka out of "Rockin' Robin", which is my favorite.

25

To my dismay, the days are again becoming shorter. Snow is piling up in staggering amounts. Med Sis decides to leave her car at home and asks Duke to drive us to the teacherage in the middle of November. We are prepared to stay there until Christmas break and stocked up on supplies. The bedroom is freezing cold so we move the bed into the kitchen close to the potbellied stove. The roads are blocked with snow most of the time, but Duke often manages to plow through with his trusty car for a visit. Soon we are practicing for our Christmas concert, which is to be held at the hall across the road from the school. Med Sis informs us that Santa is invited. I am giving him another chance to bring me my Pumpkinhead. I have done nothing bad all year and wait patiently to face him again. On the night of the concert, the hall is packed with parents and friends.

Even Duke, Mom, Daddy, and Small Sis are seated in the audience. Now we are singing "Here Comes Santa Claus," and in he bounds hollering, "What a funny looking bunch of kids! Ho! Ho! Ho!" I experience a strange feeling deep within me when I realize that his voice sounds familiar. My eyes are riveted on him as he hands out presents. Finally, he calls my name. I walk up to him, and he lifts me onto his knee. "Have you been a good girl?" he asks in that voice.

I whisper, "Yes." As he reaches for my present, I notice a string, which is attached to his white beard and which disappears behind his ear. "Thank you for the present," I add even though I know that it's not Pumpkinhead and that he has failed me, yet again. As I walk down the aisle to my seat, the pieces of another puzzle fall into placc just as they did when I saw the earthworm—there really is no Santa Claus! That man on the stage is the White Knight dressed up in a Santa Claus costume. The truth unfolds—parents give their kids presents they can afford, not Santa. Rich kids get what they want no matter how they behave. The guilt of my having been too bad to deserve Pumpkinhead is lifted from my shoulders. This is the best present ever! I don't need Pumpkinhead any more. I feel that I might even have the confidence to face the troll now. How can he be real if Santa isn't real? After the concert, as we leave the hall, I recall the daunting image of the reindeer with its eyes frozen open. I know now that it didn't belong to Santa. Grateful I no longer have to make excuses for him, I snuggle down in the back seat next to Mom with a smile on my face as Duke drives us home.

The days before Christmas are more bearable this year without my having to stew about Santa and Pumpkinhead. The main event of the holiday season is the engagement of Med Sis and Duke, who plan to marry on July 21, Small Sis's birthday. More excitement comes in the form of a card from Granny announcing that she will visit us Easter weekend. The news leaves me jumping for joy at the thought of seeing her again. Something else to look forward to is that Small Sis will be coming to stay with us at the teacherage to finish her Grade VIII at our school. Knight's farm is located on our route to the school so I know for certain that he'll be hanging around the teacherage with Duke. Med Sis spends most of her time with Duke over the holidays. I am a little bored and decide to retrieve my tricycle from under the counter where it has remained since the time it was broken by the hooligans. I drag it to my imaginary track that runs around the display table in the store. Then I perch myself on the seat in such a way as to hold the right end of the axle without the wheel up in the air. Again and again, I push it to set the two wheels in motion, as one does those of a bicycle, but manage to move only a couple of feet each time. Finally, I discover the knack of balancing my body by kind of pulling up on the right handlebar with my hand while pushing off with my right foot and then pedaling fast. Soon I am sailing around and around the table on two wheels instead of three. Anybody who watches me can't figure out how I am able to do it. Johnny predicted I would ride my trike again, and he is right. The fact that I even tried to ride it again because Johnny has control of me is a scary thought, indeed.

Having Small Sis stay with us at the teacherage is fun, and time passes more quickly than ever. We often chat and laugh late into the night—the three of us in the bed in the kitchen next to the fire crackling in the potbellied stove. We find tail trails, tiny footprints, and poop in the butter, and the scurrying sounds of little feet in the night are signs that other guests moved into our home when we were gone. Med Sis guesses they are moles. Every night, as soon as it grows dark, we can hear them rustling around. We decide that they must exterminated. Our plan is to light candles and to be ready for them with a broom, mop, and fry pan. The next night we wait for them, and they oblige by shuffling around. Med Sis lights the candles. We spot two tiny black furry creatures with long pointed noses under the table. Small Sis hops onto one of the chairs with the mop and begins to scream. She is terrified. I swat at them with the broom. With two quick whacks of the fry pan, Med Sis nails the nasty varmints. It was no pleasant task, but she had to get Small Sis to shut up somehow.

Snow is shoveled so high on both sides of the path from the teacherage to the school that I can't see over it. The weather has been bitterly cold with high winds and drifting snow. In spite of the conditions of the roads, Duke, Knight, and their friends often show up out of nowhere to visit.

One frosty Friday February morning, before leaving for school, Small Sis is goofing around on the bed. She sticks out her foot as she bounces, and her big toe catches the bottom of the stove. She giggles and reaches out to grab it, but blood is spouting from it like a fountain. Med Sis instinctively rips off a strip of the bed sheet and quickly wraps it around her foot also binding it tightly with towels. She frantically glances out the window and luckily spots the boy who starts the fire in the mornings coming into the schoolyard. She hollers, "Help, we need help! My sister cut her foot. She needs to see a doctor. Go get your dad with the caboose. Hurry!" Minutes pass slowly. Med Sis runs her fingers gently along the bottom of the potbellied heater. "It's razor sharp!" she exclaims. Then she attempts to check the toe, but it is still bleeding profusely. She decides to leave it bandaged. Finally, help arrives and we scramble into the caboose. Small Sis stretches out on a bench keeping her foot elevated, and we try to get comfortable beside her. The man gives a long, low drawl and his horses began to move, but just barely. Time drags on. When we feel the caboose making a turn, we assume we are in town. Unfortunately, we have just rounded the corner a mile from the school. We are worried. Then, like a miracle, we hear the jingle of bells from a caboose about to overtake us. Our driver pulls over, gets out, and waves it down. We transfer Small Sis into the other caboose, jump in with her, and are off like a shot. Within minutes, we arrive in town. Mom hires the taxi to take Small Sis to the hospital, and my sister accompanies her. Med Sis's handling of the incident as an emergency proved to be the right thing to do as Small Sis had severed an artery and required stitches.

26

Spring comes early. Snow begins melting all at once, and huge pools of water form on the school grounds and around the teacherage. When traveling home, we often encounter soft spots in the dirt road and the three of us try to agree on which set of ruts to take. If we choose the wrong ones, we moan in unison when the wheels begin to spin and sink as they become bogged down in the mud or when the car gets hung up on ruts that are too deep. Being stuck provides us with a valid excuse to walk over to Knight's farm for help. Sometimes we are even forced to remove our shoes or boots and walk barefoot because disengaged footwear was known to disappear in the gumbo after being slowly sucked down. Knight would drive us back with a truck or tractor and pull us out so we could continue on our way, after visiting with Small Sis, of course.

We are finally on our way home two days before Good Friday. I am so looking forward to seeing Granny. It will be a great Good Friday! When we arrive, we are surprised to learn that Mom has purchased a cow and two pigs. I can't wait to see them. The cow is in the barn in the further of the two stalls. She is black with a white curl on the bottom of her tail and turns to look at me with her large eyes as she chews her cud. Her forehead is adorned with a perfect white star. Mom sits on a stool to milk her and calls her by her name; "Bossy". The name suits her. Bossy's udder is white with black spots. I am amazed at how much milk streams from her tits into the galvanized pail. I want to try milking, too. Mom says, "Squeeze, and pull down." I follow her simple instructions and squeal with delight as more milk squirts out. When Mom finishes the job, she leaves the barn carrying a pail that is almost full of milk. I climb the ladder and check the loft. Hens, nesting in the corners, ruffle their feathers. Mom hopes to hatch her own chicks and ducklings. I jump out of the loft door and run to see the pigs. They come up to me in the pen beside the barn eagerly hoping for more food even though Mom told me she dumped slops into their trough before milking Bossy. They are pink, with sparse white coarse hair. Their snouts sniff the air and they squeal as they kick up their sharp hooves.

Daddy returns from work the next day for Easter break. "I have a surprise in my suitcase," he says. I am prepared for the spicy smell when he opens it. He reaches in and carefully lifts out a small object. "It's a transistor radio," he proudly announces. I am amazed at how tiny it is, and it doesn't even have to be plugged into a socket. I play it outside and under the counter. Then I keep the earphone plugged into my ear for most of the night listening to music from the radio station in the big town.

I am looking out the window when Granny's niece's car pulls up in front of our place. Mom, my sisters, and Smoky run out to meet Granny. I am the last to greet her because I stop at the kitchen mirror to check the golden combs in my hair making sure that they look just right. I can't believe she is there in front of me. When I stand up on my tiptoes, my cheek presses against her bosom as she hugs me close. "My, how you've grown; and you're getting prettier," she exclaims as she cups my face in her hands and examines it closely. Perhaps, Johnny was right after all. Maybe I will be a pretty woman some day. Granny is stooped over a little more but still looks, sounds, and smells the same. Mom has prepared her favorite foods for lunch, chicken soup and lemon meringue pie. Granny is desperate to hear all the news. We talk for hours. She is excited to learn about Med Sis's upcoming wedding. The drive from out west was a long one, so she moves to the sofa to relax. I bring her some of the comics I saved for the visit and also my notebook and reader. She is impressed with my handwriting. "I can see you've been practicing," she comments as she nods her head proudly.

"Soon I'll be able to use your dictionary because I'm a good reader too," I boast as I open my book and begin to read one of the stories. When I finish, I look up at her. She is beginning to doze off just as I used to when she read to me. I gently tuck a pillow under her head, cover her with a blanket, and watch her sleep.

After supper, we chat while Mom prepares the food to take to church for blessing in the morning. This year the food will be blessed right after the church service instead of at night. I open the china cabinet and bring out the Easter eggs Granny and I decorated. "We had such fun making those," she chuckles and adds, "while my hands still could." We both laugh as she draws me close and drapes her arm around me.

"I'm almost old enough to go to confession. Mom says one of my sins could be not listening to her or Daddy," I inform Granny.

"That sounds about right," agrees Granny. "One of the Ten Commandments states that thou shalt honor thy father and mother. Luke 2:41-52, The Boy Jesus at the Temple, tells a story about Jesus when he is twelve years old. Jesus and his parents are in Jerusalem for the Feast of the Passover. When his parents return home, Jesus chooses to stay behind without their permission. After three days of searching, they find him at the temple courts. His mother tells him that they were worried about him and asks him why he chose to treat them like that. His reply is that they should have known that he was at his father's house. In another story, Jesus' Mother and Brothers, in Matthew 12:46-50, Jesus' mother and brothers ask him for permission to speak to him when he is addressing a crowd." Granny pauses for a moment and comments, "It's interesting to note that Jesus had brothers." Then she continues, "He refuses to talk to his mother with his reason being that his disciples and anyone who does the will of his father in heaven are his mother and brothers." Then Granny adds, "I don't think these are examples of how to honor one's parents." I nod my head in agreement. I know I would never respond to my parents in that manner.

The next morning, I am so pleased to learn that Granny decided to come to church with Mom and me for the blessing of the food. Daddy went to visit Old Man Click earlier and still isn't back when we leave. I stand at the back of the church with Granny while the priest sings his songs and sprinkles the baskets of food with water again. The ceremony doesn't take long because he has other churches to visit. As we leave the church, we are greeted by cold, gusty winds. It has suddenly turned into a nasty day. I hope this foul weather is a not a forerunner of some unpleasant event. We pull our coats tightly around ourselves as the wind whips up dust from the road and blows shaggy clouds swiftly along overhead. From the corner of my eye, I notice Mom's mouth drop open as Old Man Click and Daddy come into view on Main Street. Old Man Click is clutching a green tablecloth in his fist just under his chin with the rest of it billowing out behind him like a cape. He is pretending to be the priest singing in a high voice. Daddy is following him, replying in song in a booming voice, just like the man in church. Unfortunately, they are unaware of our presence, otherwise they would have instantly stopped the charade, which is obviously a disgrace to my mother. The two of them must have been in the beer parlor and are on their way to Old Man Click's house. Mom keeps glancing back to watch them. By the time we arrive at our front door, they are disappearing over the tracks. Mom is furious and spouts her familiar words, "What will people think?"

We are all on edge and eat lunch in silence. I sense Granny's discomfort. Even though people drop by to visit her, the afternoon passes slowly, . We aren't very hungry at suppertime either. It is very late when Daddy comes in the front door. He must have gone back to the beer parlor after he took Old Man Click home because he is drunk. Mom starts in on him in Ukrainian as he sits down at the table in the store section. I am standing between Med Sis and Granny next to the counter. Small Sis is standing with Mom. In an attempt to save the situation, Med Sis says, "It's okay…"

"You think you're smart because you wear glasses," snaps Daddy cutting her off. He glares at Granny and continues his barrage yelling, "And you are giving her too many bright ideas." He swears and hurls insults at all of us in Ukrainian.

"Shut up and get out," Mom hollers. In response, Daddy picks up a ketchup bottle and slams it into the metal tabletop so hard that it forms a dent. Suddenly, he lunges forward. A policeman appears out of nowhere and grabs Daddy by the arm.

"You're coming with me," he commands as he forces Daddy outside and into a police car. We run after them. "You can pick him up on Monday at the courthouse," he calls. When the car pulls away, I burst into tears hugging Granny and Med Sis. How could the people I care about the most be involved in something like this? Why did this have to happen? It doesn't make sense. I worry about what might happen to my daddy and want to be with him. Granny's face is riddled with guilt.

"It's not your fault," I sob through my tears. "It's the beer," I add recalling the fights by the hotel. Time passes and we sit there saying nothing. Finally, we decide to go to bed and deal with the mess in the morning.

We gather in the kitchen after a restless night. Granny is upset about having to leave in the afternoon without knowing how things will turn out next day in the big town. Med Sis promises to write and fill her in on the details. We find out from Hattie, who conveniently drops in, that a neighbor had been walking by, heard the ruckus, and alerted the policeman who happened to be checking out the drunks at the hotel. He had been watching us through the window. As soon as Daddy made the move toward us, he intervened. If Hattie knew, we could be sure that the whole town knew what had happened by now, too.

Our anguish is interrupted by a cheeping noise. Mom rushes to a box on the cook stove. She pulls back the towel covering it to reveal a little chick still wet from the inside of the egg from which it has just hatched. It is struggling to stand up on its skinny legs. There are cracks in two of the other eggs and also in one of the duck eggs. Mom had placed the box over the water reservoir to keep the eggs warm. This is a wonderful Easter experience, and the timing is perfect as it takes our minds off our misery momentarily. Within a couple of hours, a duckling and two more chicks hatch as we watch. In no time, the little ones are dry and fluffy. I can't decide whether the duckling or the chicks are cuter. I like the duckling's rounded bill more than the chicks' pointed beaks. I am afraid to hold them at first. Once I become accustomed to their movement, I am able to confidently cup them with my hands, which seems to offer them security because they stop struggling, close their eyes, and fall asleep.

All too soon, Granny's niece arrives to pick her up. Assuring Granny that everything is going to be all right also makes us feel better. As she hugs me, she whispers, "I promise I'll be back soon." She waves good-bye from the car window. I wave, just a little wave, and watch until the car disappears from sight as it rounds the corner by the church. I decide to confide in Big Brother.

"Johnny, I am so upset about everything that's happened," I sob.

"I know. It's too bad that you had to see two people you

love so much go through that," he replies.

"I wish Mom and Daddy would get along better. I heard rumors that Daddy left a wife with a son and daughter in the old country, and that's why Mom treats him the way she does."

"When your dad left them, his plan was to bring them over after he had a job and was settled. But the Communists came into power, and everything was sealed off. Stalin starved millions of Ukrainians and had many killed—eleven million in all. Your grandfather was one of the first to be executed because he was a schoolteacher. He was accused of conducting classes in their church. Your dad's entire family perished, and that is why he hasn't heard from them for over twenty years. Your mom also accuses him of gambling away most of his paycheck, and you know she hates gambling. That's another reason why they don't get along. Don't worry. Your dad will be okay. You'll see tomorrow. There was a reason for his coming to Canada. If he wouldn't have come here, you wouldn't have been born," he concludes. I leave the rock with my head down, feeling upset and sad about Daddy's family. I would like to have another sister, but I am not too sure about having a brother. Thank goodness, I have Johnny. I decide that he is the only brother I needed. His words give me the strength to face tomorrow.

We are all visibly shaken as we enter the courthouse. Daddy is waiting for us when we file into the large room. After we are seated, the judge asks him if he has any remorse for what he has done. Of course, he is terribly ashamed for all the heartache he has put us through. With tears in his eyes, he promises never do such a thing again. The judge rules that we can take him home. I know Mom will never forgive him. As soon as we get back, the first thing Med Sis does is to write Granny a letter telling her that everything is fine and that Daddy apologizes to everyone for getting drunk and for saying all those horrible things to her.

The next day, one of the pigs jumps out of the pen. Trumpeting a repeated high-pitched squeal, it clomps down Main Street at a brisk rate with Med Sis in close pursuit and Daddy running after her. Two young fellows, who are standing in front of the corner store, find the incident amusing but pitch in to help them corner the pig in front of the train station. After one of them slips a rope around its neck, my sister coaxes it back home with a corncob. Daddy nails chicken wire around the top of the pen and has to extend it after the pig's second escape. Things are pretty much back to normal. In order to ease any tension between us, my dad apologizes to me several times for his actions. He doesn't have to because I forgave him when I saw him in the courthouse. Time always passes quickly when he is at home. Having the chicks and ducklings to play with also keeps me occupied. Before I know it, Daddy is gone and I am back at the teacherage with my sisters.

27

My eighth birthday happens to fall on a Saturday, and we are at home again. Most of the kids in town gather in front of our place in the afternoon. One of them rides over on an enormous bicycle. It's a boy's bike, with paint worn off the fenders and a rectangular carrier constructed of rusting strips of heavy metal. Everyone takes a turn riding it. When they are done, I shyly ask, "May I, please, try?" I grab the handlebar that is offered to me and stretch my leg under the bar to the pedal on the other side.

Med Sis hollers, "Just push off and keep on pedaling." I follow her instructions to get the wheels turning. Then I place my other foot on the pedal and move ahead. She runs with me for some distance, gives me a push, and lets go of the seat. It's much like riding my tricycle on two wheels, but I'm moving so much faster. The air feels cool and damp on my face as my hair is whipped away from my forehead. It had just showered, and a rainbow appears with one end hidden behind the church on the corner. As I pass the church, I see the end of the rainbow straight ahead. I am sure I can reach it. I pedal as hard as I can, drop the bike, and run into the rays in the shallow ditch. There is no pot of gold at the end of the rainbow. I am thoroughly disgusted, so I hop on the bike and pedal back controlling it as though I have been riding it forever.

"Where have you been for so long?" someone asks. I don't answer because nobody would believe me anyway. I must speak to Johnny. I hand over the bike and head for the rock upset with the world and all of its lies.

"Johnny, what is going on? I can't be a boy like everybody wanted because I don't have an earthworm; there is no Santa Claus; and now I find out that there is no pot of gold at the end of the rainbow. Maybe there is no God and no heaven or hell either. Maybe we're wasting our time worrying about whether we are doing right or wrong because God is watching us, and spending money on churches and priests for nothing. I hope when I die that there is no heaven or hell and that things will be the way they were before I was born—that there will be nothing there, just nothing," I confess choking back tears.

"I must admit that life is full of disappointments, but

listen closely to this saying, 'The past is history; the future is a mystery; and the present is a fleeting gift.' Life is short so try to do your best at whatever comes your way, and you will never have any regrets. You will always put everyone else's needs ahead of your own; and timing will seem to be off, as events unfold in your life. However, one day, you will reap your rewards—one day that will be a long time coming." I treasure Johnny's words as I recall them at night in bed. Most of all, I want the troll not to be real; but I don't believe that anyone, not even Johnny, could convince me that he isn't.

On the May long weekend we are invited to meet Duke's parents and younger brother. Duke comes to pick us up. Their farm is about twenty-five miles away. He steers the car along the dusty road curving around a lake which sparkles in the bright sunlight. He counts down the miles as he drives: "Ten, five, three, two, one." Then we cross a wooden bridge, which stretches over a fast-flowing river, and turn into his farmyard. It is like entering a "Ma and Pa Kettle" movie. The house sports a weather-beaten exterior, which has never been painted. The roof sags. Rusty pails and pieces of machinery litter the yard. The verandah obviously isn't used as the main entrance, because tall grass and brush surrounds it. Duke's mother greets us at the back door that opens into a porch. She looks a bit like Ma Kettle. I expect her to bellow like Ma and am taken aback by her voice that is much softer and her words precisely pronounced. She deliberately makes a point of portraying herself as being very English. Her white hair is pulled back into a roll at the back of her head and seems to want to spring out of the combs that hold it in place. She wears trifocals and holds her head like a peacock or a turkey, feigning royalty. Her white skin is very thin and forms small rippling wrinkles on her neck. She is wearing a dark flowered dress partially hidden by a faded yellow bibbed apron, brown stockings, and black laced shoes with thick heels. When her hands aren't moving, they dangle from her wrists in front of her. Duke's father is sitting in the living room smoking a pipe. He comes into the kitchen to shake hands with us. His fingers are gnarled, and his shoulders stoop forward. The white wavy hair that is combed back from his forehead matches the full, unruly eyebrows, which protrude over piercing green eyes. He wears loose overalls over a plaid shirt and speaks in a weak drawl very much like Pa Kettle's.

Duke's mother prepares us a lovely meal, which we eat sitting around the kitchen table covered with a red and white checkered tablecloth. Built-in cupboards run along one side of the room, and an old cook stove adorned with chrome stands near the entrance to the porch. Several dark cabinets decorated with intricate carved designs and glass doors, protecting the delicate china and stemware inside, line the living room walls. The rocking chair is in the living room, not out on the verandah like in the movies. Another cushioned chair and sofa, a wood-burning heater, and a high-backed piano accompany it. Duke's brother comes home later in the evening and introduces himself. He favors his mom, while Duke is the spitting image of his dad. His short hair is not as curly as his brother's. He has twinkling blue eyes and a mischievous smile. Since he missed the meal, he helps himself to leftovers.

I am drawn outside by the sound of rushing water and follow a beaten path onto the rocky shore of the river, which is the first one I have ever seen. The water level is high from spring run-off, and the current is swift under the bridge. There is absolutely no chance of a troll's surviving under it. Some of the jagged rocks are big, but are not as big as mine. It is a beautiful spot; I sit on the trunk of a poplar tree, which has fallen parallel to the river, and stare out over the churning water for a long time.

Later that night, Duke plays the piano with much glee and gusto. His fingers bounce with ease along the yellowing ivory keys as he plays by ear. He taps his feet on the floor but still manages to force down the worn metal pedals at the bottom of the piano, whenever necessary, without missing a beat. As we all crowd around and sing along, he plays "Roll out the Barrel" and then slows the pace with "Let Me Call You Sweetheart." After the performance, his brother sets up a card table and brings out a board game. I am reluctant to play at first but am soon squealing with delight as I knock his men off the board. The game proves to be even more fun than playing cards. Time flies. We are treated to tea and sweets before we leave, and it is way past midnight by the time Duke drives us home. He has to travel all the way back by himself but doesn't seem to mind. I overhear Mom talking to Med Sis as they prepare for bed. Mom is questioning her decision to get married, wondering whether she is making the right choice—to live in that old house on that dilapidated farm with his parents watching her every move. If my opinion meant anything, I would advise her to keep on teaching because nothing could beat having your own money to spend. Besides, she could really teach.

28

It is a warm day near the end of May. Everyone in the classroom is restless, longing to be outdoors. Med Sis, who grows impatient with the whispering behind her back as she writes on the blackboard, turns around and sputters, "The next person to make a sound when they don't have permission will stay after school." She turns back to the board and continues to write. Behind me sits the boy who is always doing something to annoy me. He picks this moment, of all moments, to lift the seat of my desk high off the floor and swing me from side to side. I turn around and am greeted by the familiar sneer on his face.

I angrily mime the words, "Quit it." Unfortunately, my sister whirls around in time to catch me talking to him; and her mouth drops open in surprise.

"You must stay after school," she gulps. I feel more betrayed than she does because I don't have the opportunity to defend myself. I run out of the school toward the teacherage with my sister at my heels.

She tries to grab me, but I struggle with her sobbing, "That boy sitting behind me picked my desk off the floor and swung it around to get me in trouble with you. I hate him. I just can't stand him."

I calm down when she hugs me and whispers, "I understand but, please, come back and stay after school for my sake. Everybody knows what happened, and they can judge for themselves." She walks back and I follow far behind. When classes are over, the other kids leave. My punishment is to last for half an hour. I reluctantly proceed to draw and read. After about fifteen minutes of silence, Med Sis glances at me over the book she is reading and grins at me. I grin back, and then we both burst into laughter.

"We have to do this more often," she giggles.

One muggy Friday morning in June, I search unsuccessfully for something to wear to school. My only piece of clean clothing is a jumper with a black velveteen top, open sides, and a plaid skirt gently gathered at the waist. Everything else is in the laundry bag hanging on the back of the bedroom door. I don't want to wear it because I am afraid somebody might be able see in along the sides if I bend in a certain way. Med Sis advises me to go ahead and wear it assuring me that it will be fine. Sure enough, when we are playing outside at recess, the boy with the sneer keeps taunting, "I can see your tits. I can see your tits." I hate that guy and his beloved earthworm. At our age, my tits aren't any different from his. I don't give him the satisfaction of a response. Instead, I stomp back to the teacherage, rip off the jumper, and find something from the laundry bag to wear for the remainder of the afternoon.

We drive into town that evening for the weekend. The roads are dry for a change and very dusty. We find Mom in the process of sewing the bridesmaids' gowns for the wedding. Yards of pale gold and pale green fabric are draped over the sofa and armchair in the living room. She is just adding the final touches to the gown for the maid of honor. When she is done, Med Sis picks it up and holds it in front of herself, admiring the masterpiece as she swings around in the middle of floor. The gown is pale green with netting over taffeta. The top has straps like a sundress with netting shirred over a fitted bodice. The floor length skirt is generously gathered at the waist with yards and yards of netting and taffeta. It is beautiful. The bridesmaids' gowns will be of the same style but in the pale gold color. I am too old to be a flower girl and too young to be a junior bridesmaid, but I am still included in the wedding party. My dress is to be pale gold, of the same style as the others, and will be sewn last. Mom works without a pattern on the treadle sewing machine. She should be a famous designer— her talent is wasted here in this end-of-the-line place.

Med Sis purchased her wedding dress in the big town. When she brings it home, we all watch as she unzips the satin bag protecting it. The gown is made of French lace, featuring a fitted bodice with tiny pearl buttons down the front, a delicate Peter Pan collar, and long sleeves. The skirt is gently gathered at the waist and falls to the floor. Its lace chapel-length train matches the veil. Med Sis models it for us. "Glamorous" and "gorgeous" are the only words worthy of describing it. I decide to consult with Johnny about a couple of things and race with Smoky all the way to the big rock. Without giving Johnny a chance to greet me, I ask, "Johnny, I want to know if I will be a bride someday and wear a gown like my sister's?"

"Hi, Little Sister. I know you're excited about the wedding. Every little girl dreams about being a bride. Getting their daughters married off when they are young is the goal of every mother in this town." He pauses for a moment as if trying to gather some thoughts together and then continues, "I can see you trying on a beautiful low-luster satin gown which, as you turn around slowly in front of a three way mirror, you decide is the wedding dress for you. The saleslady comments that you would make a perfect model for wedding gowns. She hands you a bouquet of red silk roses and snaps a Polaroid picture of you as she does with everyone who buys a gown from her. A couple of days later, people in town somehow learn that you have the picture. A man asks to see it. As he studies it, he informs you that you are not good enough for the guy you are going to marry. Another man repeats his words; and you are, therefore, inclined to believe them. These degrading comments will haunt you for years. You will never forget them or forgive those insecure so-and-so's, but you will find a way to get even with them."

"That nasty boy at school today was making fun of me and telling me I had no tits. I want to know if I ever will— have tits, I mean," I blurt out before I have time to change my mind about raising the subject.

"I can see your mom asking you to run to the store for a loaf of bread," relates Johnny in a tone that indicates that he is drawing his words from obscurity. "You know that it's easier and faster for you to go than it is for her. She hands you some coins, and you are out the door. As the owner of the business gives you the loaf of bread, you place the money on the counter. Instead of picking up the coins, he leans over and grabs you by your breast. In spite of the shock you experience, you react quickly by grabbing the money and the bread and running out of the building. There is nothing he can do about getting the money or the bread back—which fixes him—or does it? You make a point of never going into that place alone again if nobody else is in there.

"At another time and in another place, I see you standing in a group of people of all ages looking out onto the horizon. Someone has binoculars and believes he can see a UFO, which he describes as being a round object in the orange sky. Others take turns with the binoculars; but, when they fail to spot anything, they slowly wander back to the house. One old man is left looking through the binoculars. He waves motioning for you to come and have a look. You sense you shouldn't, but Med Sis tells you to go ahead as she disappears into the house. You raise the binoculars to your eyes while he stands behind you pointing toward the west. All of a sudden, his gnarled fingers are on your breasts. You jerk your arms down knocking his hands away. The binoculars fall to the ground in slow motion, but you do nothing to stop them. Instead, feeling violated and disgusted, you run for safety and make a point of never again being left alone with that pervert either. I only told you this as a warning so that you'll better prepared when my predictions become reality." I leave the rock without saying good night to Johnny. I have so much information to process that I forget about the troll for once as I head upstairs.

The weather on the last day of our stay at the teacherage is an expression of my sentiments. My heart is crying inside. Outdoors, it continues to pour even harder than it has all week. The school grounds are flooded. After Med Sis locks the school door for the very last time, we wait in the teacherage for Knight, who promised to come and help us move. The car is already loaded with our belongings, but we have more boxes for him. He finally arrives on a tractor with a small trailer attached behind it.

We hastily pile the boxes onto the trailer, which he covers with a tarp. He is wearing a raincoat and high tops, but we are drenched by the time we hop into Med Sis's car and follow the tractor out of the schoolyard. Memories of the year spent here flash through my mind. I don't want to leave. As we make the turn, I forget about leaving and focus on the water hiding the road ahead from view. Knight comes over to give my sister instructions. "Just follow close behind me; don't stop; and you'll be okay." The car cuts through the water like a beetle. Luckily, it is set up high on its wheels. Med Sis keeps her foot on the gas; and, sure enough, we make the corner without stalling. After that, the deep ditches on the sides of the road have handled the run-off, making the remainder of the road visible again.

29

Several days before the wedding, women from town meet at our place to help prepare food for the supper. They cook something different each day including perogies, cabbage rolls, and meatballs. Home smells almost as good as it does on holy holidays. I try to help my mom as much as I can and run to the store and the egg station whenever she needs something.

Then the big day arrives. Med Sis looks radiant in her gown. I dress up in my golden gown, matching gauntlets, and a headpiece that Mom designed by gathering a band of netting on a piece of wire. Then I join the bridesmaids. We pick our bouquets out of a long, shallow box. Mine is a nosegay of artificial daises surrounded by green leaves.

The wedding ceremony is to be held in the big town. The girls voice their concerns about creasing their gowns as they climb into the wedding cars decorated with white flowers made by the female members of the wedding party. Even I learned how to make them—cut tissues, fold them like an accordion, tie a string around the middle, and fluff them out.

The church is much older, fancier, and larger than Mom's. After the ceremony, we drive to a studio for our appointment with the photographer. Then we begin our trip back home. We travel in three cars honking in town and then whenever we pass a farmhouse. After a short break at home, we head for the hall beside Mom's church for the meal and dancing. I imagine myself as being a ray of sunlight in my golden gown. When darkness falls, I am convinced I can light up the night as I run around with other little girls. Boys chase after us on the stage, through the hall, and outside. I love the fiddle music and even have the pleasure of dancing with Duke and Knight. Thanks to Jigger-r-r-ram, I am such a good dancer! After I eat my fill of perogies and pickled beets with horseradish, I fall asleep on the pile of coats and jackets at the back of the hall. When I wake up, I am at home in bed and still wearing my gown. I never want to take it off.

Med Sis and Duke leave for their honeymoon, and the realization that she isn't going to be around any more is sinking in fast. All of her belongings are gone because they will be living at that farm. We had grown very close at the teacherage. When they return, I look forward to her visits. I often stay at that farm for a week at a time where I learn new card and board games. We always play late into the night until the summer holiday is over. Then I am back in the big school again. The Grade III's are in the same room as the Grade I's and II's with the same teacher I had in Grade I. I missed Med Sis's small school because the girls had formed their little groups, and I just didn't belong. However, a boy in Grade II seems interested in becoming my friend. His family moved into town when I was staying at the teacherage. He follows me everywhere.

One day, I am in the bower playing by myself, as I often do. It is different from the bush at the teacherage. I feel safe here because I know what is on either side of the bower. I have Grandy with me and am setting up her sleeping quarters when I am startled by the snap of a twig right behind me. I whirl around and am, at first, relieved to see that it is only the new boy. I wonder how long he has been watching me. "Why are you here?" I ask beginning to feel uncomfortable with his presence.

"I'll show you my thing if you pay me five cents," he replies.

"No, I've already seen one and I don't need to see another one," I fume, wishing he'd go away.

"How about one cent?" he asks. I am about to boot him out when the dark-haired boy who teased me about getting a strap every day at school jumps out from behind a bush

He pushes the small boy out of the way and hollers, "Scram." The boy backs away, turns, and runs. "You're a cutie," he croons and pauses for a moment as he reaches out and touches my hair. "Maybe you'd like to come over to that shack over there and have some fun with me and my friends later, and you can see more of this." He unzips his pants and pulls out his earthworm and starts moving his hand back and forth over it. It looks like the slugs I saw in the garbage heap behind the toilet. I stand there with my feet rooted to the ground. When I come to my senses, I realize I must get out of the bower. If anything happens, I know I'll be blamed. I dart past him and run all the way to the kitchen door without once looking back. When I reach the bedroom, I begin to tremble. I know I can't tell anybody about what happened. Much later, I sneak out of the house and circle around the deep grass keeping watch on the shack in the distance. I creep up, crouching low to the ground, and hide in some bushes. Sure enough, I see some girls enter the shack. Then the dark-haired boy and his friends follow them in. The window is too high up for me to see inside. Besides, it is covered with a thin curtain. However, I hear giggling and that boy speaking in a low voice. I have a pretty good idea of what they are doing in there, and I leave while it is still safe to do so.

30

The Christmas season is upon us again. The weather is milder than usual, and snow blankets the town creating a winter wonderland. Daddy is home for three weeks, and everyone has forgiven him for his part in the Easter incident, except for Mom, of course. Small Sis and I decide to exchange goofy Christmas presents and spend days collecting items from around the house and wrapping them in comics from the newspaper. Anxious to open them, we are up early Christmas morning. My sister howls with laughter when she opens the first gift, the guts from an old pencil sharpener. I tear the paper off mine to find an empty cold cream jar. It is hilarious. The hullabaloo continues as we take turns opening the gifts. She ends up with a box of empty peanut shells, one brown stocking, a mousetrap, and a handle from a potato masher. My remaining presents are some rusty bobby pins, a comb with missing teeth, and a bag of metal bottle caps. It is the Merriest Christmas ever. Who needs Santa Claus?

On a previous visit, Med Sis proudly presented Mom with a turkey she raised herself. Later that morning, Mom stuffs the bird and slides it into the oven. Daddy stokes the fire regularly to keep the oven the right temperature. I stick around the house all day savoring the smell of the roasting turkey coming from the kitchen. Med Sis, Duke, his parents, and his brother join us for supper. The turkey is tender and full of flavor. Even the dressing is delicious, and I enjoy it almost as much as the pickled beets with horseradish. Mom's face beams with pride when we brag that she is as good a cook as she is a seamstress. After supper, I open my Christmas gift from Med Sis and her husband. It is a three-piece dresser set consisting of a mirror, brush, and comb. The mirror has a plastic handle engraved with an intricate pattern of triangles. The back of the mirror features a painting of a brown-haired girl wearing a blue dress and a wide brimmed hat decorated with a white ribbon to which is attached a sprig of red flowers. Med Sis says, "I chose the set because the girl looks like you." I smile and lower my head. Mom and Duke's mother visit while the others play a card game called "Canasta." I sit beside my sister and watch, because they decided the game was too complicated for me to play.

I am introduced to chickenpox in the middle of winter. Red spots appear on my chest and back with a few dotting my legs and arms. Mom isolates me in the bedroom at the kitchen entrance. During my recovery, I can't lie still and practice various stunts on my bed including standing on my head, doing backward somersaults, and bending over backwards until my hands reached the mattress and then returning to a standing position. I become very good at the latter and can't wait to try it outside when the snow is gone.

The Easter break begins quietly because, I suppose, we are all thinking about what happened the year before. Knight comes over to our house for the first time to visit with Small Sis. Mom is busy in the kitchen. He asks her what she is making to which she replies, "Paska." He laughs so hard that tears roll down his cheeks. Small Sis explains that Mom is just making Easter bread and wants to know what is so funny. He whispers something in her ear, and she chuckles too.

Moments after he leaves, my sister, who is hardly able to

contain herself, blurts out, "You know what, Mom? In Finn, 'paska' means 'poop'." Imagine her, our mother, telling him that she was making poop. Mom laughs until she cries. It is so refreshing to hear her laugh again that we just listen.

Shortly after my ninth birthday, Czar of the East sends train tickets for Mom, Small Sis, and me to come and visit them in the summer because his wife is homesick and missing her family. No birthday present could have been any better! I am so excited that I immediately begin to plan what I will pack in Frizzy's suitcase. On the other hand, Small Sis is concerned about leaving Knight for too long because they are now seeing each other.

The school year is coming to an end. I pass but am not looking forward to going into the next grade because everyone says that the Grade VI teacher is very strict and that his specialty is giving kids the strap. Long ago, I nicknamed him "Mr. Mustache" because he has a narrow bristly growth under his nose. He is a short, stocky man, who wears dark suits and smells of a mixture of tobacco and strong shaving lotion. His thinning hair is combed back in dark sparse streaks. He teaches Grades IV through VIII and expects over fifty students to crowd into his room next fall. I dread being one of them but promise myself I am not going to think about him. For now, nothing is going to spoil my summer holiday out east.

31

The beginning of July is hot and muggy. I spend most of my time packing my belongings into Frizzy's suitcase, which Mom and I decided to share. I wish I could take Grandy, but she is just too big. I will take a smaller drink-and-wet rubber dolly that I can easily carry and play with on the train. A couple of days before our departure, Knight comes over to bid farewell to Small Sis. He is all dusty and dirty from working in the field. They decide to take me to the lake with them where they can spend some time together and escape the heat. I am so excited. I have never before been to the beach. I saw Duke's river and the lake on the way to his farm, but I can't believe how big this lake is. Water stretches as far as my eyes can see. I run into the water after Small Sis and Knight. They have bathing suits, but I don't, so I plunge in wearing my shorts and blouse. The water is warm, and I am amazed at how well it buoys me up. Knight is a strong swimmer. He swims along the shore for some distance and then back again, shampoos his hair, and washes himself off with soap. Then he carries my sister around on his shoulders and occasionally plops her into the water to make her scream. They are in a world of their own frolicking in the rays of the setting sun. Even I can see they are in "lo-o-o-ve." I create my own fun trying to swim by springing off the sandy bottom with my feet and kicking them while I move my arms. As I experiment, I find I make the most progress underwater and practice keeping my eyes open. Darkness has fallen by the time we get home, and Mom is already pacing the floor because she is worried about us.

An unexpected visitor appears at out door the evening before we are to leave on our trip. The storekeeper, to whom Mom owes a small amount of money for groceries, heard we were going out east and assumed we weren't coming back. "I want your bill paid in full," he threatens in a menacing tone. Mom gives him the money from the till, which is, obviously, not enough because he confiscates some cleaning products left behind by a huckster to make up the balance.

After he leaves, I hug Mom around the waist and cry, "He's so mean."

"Yeah," she agrees. "Don't you worry. I have $2.75 in my purse. I'll make a big lunch and we'll be okay."

Early the next morning, Duke and Med Sis drive us to the station near the big town. As we stand on the platform, the train, with its whistle hooting continuously, breaks through the dense fog. Med Sis gives us each a hug while the conductor lifts our suitcases into a coach. After hurrying on board, we choose two seats facing each other near the washroom. I barely have time to wave to my sister, who is holding back tears, as the train lurches forward. She should have been the one to go because she would remember the town out east from living there for a year. Soon she is out of sight, and the train keeps chugging along. The scenery is the same for miles, flat fields, fence posts, and the occasional clump of trees. The train seems to stop at every building along the way. Our coach is almost empty so my sister moves across the aisle crying because she is already missing her boyfriend. Mom orders me to nudge her if she starts to snore. I am curious to see what is in the washroom and open the strange metal door. I figure out how to work the lever on the sink and see water come out of a tap for the first time in my life. Then, another first for me is flushing the toilet after I have a pee. On the door, I notice a sign, which reads: "PLEASE DO NOT FLUSH TOILET WHEN TRAIN IS STANDING IN STATION". Beside the mirror hangs a long cylinder of paper drinking cups, meaning I can have a drink any time without having to run to the well for it. When I come out of the washroom, a little girl, who is about three, approaches me wanting to play. Her mom, who is sitting in the middle of the coach, opens a small suitcase filled with boiled wieners, rolls, peanut butter and cheese sandwiches, bananas, assorted fruits, cookies, pop, and juice. "Would you like something to eat?" she asks.

"Thank you, but I'm full," I reply even though I have that hollow feeling in my stomach and know I could, probably, eat all of it. I play with the girl for a while and then return to my seat. Mom has her head back and is snoring loudly through her mouth. There is nobody around, and the train is noisy so I choose to let her sleep. Besides, her snoring reassures me that she is still alive.

Finally, we pull into the big city where we are to transfer trains. I have never before seen so many cars, people, or big buildings. There will be an eight-hour wait at the station, but we are accustomed to passing time slowly. In the terminal, Mom chooses a bench, and I cautiously venture out from it in different directions by myself, making sure I note the surroundings so I won't get lost. Within an hour, I know were everything is. I especially like the area where travelers board trains. Signs with large black numbers identify tracks to different destinations. The bathroom is huge, with more stalls and sinks than I could ever imagine. I watch customers eating in the cafeteria and restaurant and wonder how they can afford such expensive food as prices are listed in the windows. We aren't able to spend any of our $2.75, which we must save in case of an emergency.

For supper, mom allows us to eat some of our

sandwiches that are already drying out, and then we catch our train. It is crowded, but we are lucky enough to get two seats facing each other again. Across the aisle sits an obese gray-haired woman with a chubby older boy. They are a strange looking pair surrounded by puffy pillows and patched quilts. There is an alarm clock on their windowsill. Various-sized suitcases with rope tied around each of them are stacked on the rack overhead. They have all sorts of food and eat continuously. I try not to stare, but they provide my entertainment until the movement and sound of the train lull me to sleep. When I awaken, it is dark outside. Rivulets of rain force their way down the outside of the windows. The coach is dimly lit with small round fixtures on the ceiling above the seats. Passengers bedding down for the night are silently turning them off, one by one. I lean over to check the time on our neighbor's alarm clock. It is only midnight. I feel a chill and pull my blue corduroy jacket with the white flannelette lining up under my chin and hold my dolly closely under it. I curl up next to my sister who is sleeping with her head on a pillow propped up between the back of her seat and the window.

Suddenly, I wake up feeling nauseated and dash to the washroom. Being sick to my stomach convinces me that the motion of the train over such an extended period of time is making me ill. Several more trips to the washroom leave me weak and tired. I drink water from the little cups to moisten my dry mouth and throat and sleep all that day and night. Late in the afternoon, we arrive at the big city out east where we are to transfer again. We have only a few seconds to board our next train, but we arrive within hours at our destination, the city of the Czars. It is dark.; luckily, the station agent is still in his office. Mom finds Big Sis's phone number in her purse, and the agent makes a quick call. Minutes later, Czar pulls up in the familiar water beetle car with Czar I and Czar II in their pajamas and sitting in the front seat. He greets us with good news. My sister gave birth to another son, Czar III, the day we left home and will be released from the hospital in the morning.

Even though the night is terribly hot and humid, I feel better as a result of being freed from the motion and sound of the train. Czar loads our luggage into the trunk, and we climb into the back seat because the two boys want to remain in the front with their dad. He tells us to roll down the windows as we leave the station and points out the canal that runs parallel to the street. Bright lights on posts dot the entire length of the waterway, and benches line both sides. The scent of flowers, blooming in wooden baskets, permeates the air and enters the car as we roll along. The streets are paved, not dusty like ours. He stops the car to wait for a bridge to come down. A ship is passing through the canal, so large machines lift the bridge, stopping traffic. When the ship is clear, the bridge comes down. We proceed over it, through downtown, and past the tube manufacturing plant where he works.

As we turn into their driveway, the headlights illuminate a square two-story house on a corner lot lined with tall maple trees. A hedge, trimmed to approximately two feet in height with large ball-shaped accents every six feet or so in front of the trees, gives the yard a well-manicured appearance. The exterior lights of the house and two-car garage are on, and the moon is full and bright, making the night seem like day. We each grab a suitcase and enter the house through the back door. Steps lead from the landing into the basement. We ascend the three steps into the kitchen, which has a white refrigerator and stove, a red arborite and chrome table with matching chairs, built-in cupboards, and a sink with taps for running water. We follow Czar though the living room with its shining hardwood floor. It is furnished with a sofa and chair, a coffee table, an end table with a telephone, and a television—the first one I have ever seen. There are also two bedrooms and a bathroom with a white tub, sink, and toilet on the main floor. We are to have the second floor to ourselves and follow him up the stairs. Between two large bedrooms nestles a kitchenette with cupboards and a sink. A small bathroom with only a toilet is located next to the upstairs landing. Mom and I decide to share the north room so that my sister can have the other bedroom to herself.

I breathe a sigh of relief when Czar invites us downstairs for something to eat. I am famished. We invade the kitchen along with the boys. Mom wants tea and finds the kettle, fills it with water from the tap, and sets it on the stove. Czar turns a knob and flames come shooting out from under the kettle, which takes me completely by surprise. As he pulls bread, peanut butter, and jam from the cupboards and a glass bottle of milk from the refrigerator, he explains that the stove burns natural gas. The surroundings remind me of the cutout paper appliances and furniture from the catalogues I play with at home. I never tasted such fresh bread since Field Day. The peanut butter is smooth with no stale oil on top. Even the milk tastes special, not like our cow milk. I eat three pieces of bread with peanut butter and jam and want more but decide I'd better not make a pig of myself. The boys stuff their crusts into the slot in the table where the sides pull out to extend it. As I lie in bed upstairs in the dark I think I could have eaten those crusts and the rest of the bread. I am no longer feeling nauseated and rub my full tummy, feeling so much better. Mom is already snoring next to me. I fall asleep listening to the roar of engines and whistling of trains nearby, thankful that I am no longer on one of them.

In the morning, Czar goes to the hospital to pick up my

sister and the new baby. The boys turn on the television and begin watching cartoons. I join them sitting a safe distance away. I still haven't gotten rid of my negative feelings towards Czar I as a result of the bottle cap incident. Soon the new son is home, and he lets everybody know it. Big Sis can't get him to stop screaming and concludes that the house is just too hot for him. We crowd around as she takes off his clothes. His face is beet-red, and his skinny legs stick out of his diaper flailing about as he wails. After a few minutes, I return to watch cartoons with his brothers.

I quickly become an expert at watching television and even pick out programs from the TV guide. My favorites are "Rin Tin Tin," "The Cisco Kid," "The Lone Ranger," "Zorro," and "Fury." I watch everything, even the commercials. Mom begins to complain about my watching too much television. I am just making sure I watch enough of it to last me a while, because there will be no television at home. Whatever time I don't spend in front of the television, I spend in the bathtub. I lather up my hair with shampoo, climb into the tub, turn on the cold water tap, and rinse my hair under it. Because the weather is so hot, the water coming out of the cold water tap is lukewarm. Then I use a little soap and fill the tub up with bubbles. I always have my rubber dolly and two of the Czars' orange plastic fish with me. I can squeeze bubbles out of the holes in the doll's mouth and bum as I make her ride around on the fish. I play until somebody knocks on the door and orders me out of the tub. Usually, my hands and feet are wrinkled up like a prune. I love feeling squeaky clean as I dry myself off in a big fluffy towel. Just like with the TV, I am just making sure that I bathe enough to last me a while because there will be no bathtub with running water at home. I also spend time playing with my doll in the shade on the grassy slope that extends away from the foundation of the house. Big Sis gave me some flannelette which I cut into the shapes of undershirts, diapers, and nighties and pin to the baby doll.

32

Czar takes it upon himself to entertain us. On his first day off, he drives us to a nearby town to visit his relatives. It is at their place that I eat my first slice of pizza. It tastes strange; but, with every bite, I enjoy it more and more.

He often takes us to the canal in order to escape the heat and to give Big Sis a chance to be alone with the baby. The canal is too deep for kids to swim in. Czar, on the other hand, allows us take turns flipping a quarter into the water so that he can dive in and retrieve it before it hits the bottom. We cheer every time he comes out of the water and holds the coin up in his fingers for all of us to see.

Small Sis makes friends with a girl who lives across the street. They are almost the same age, and she has five younger brothers. One day, she invites my sister to accompany her to the community outdoor pool. They offer to take me along, but I have no bathing suit. Mom sews me one using a piece of leftover fabric, a bright blue swatch of cotton decorated with yellow ducklings. She takes a pair of my panties and covers them with the fabric gathering it at the leg and waist openings, attaches a top with straps to go over my shoulders, and sews on yellow buttons to close the opening at the back. I wriggle into it and spin around in front of the mirror. I like it more than the ones I saw in the catalogue. Soon we are at the pool, which is overcrowded.

Keeping track of my sister and her friend is difficult, and there just isn't enough space to practice kicking off the bottom to try to swim. A couple of days later, Czar take us to a lake to compensate for our disappointment at the pool. I am eager to wear my bathing suit again. A sandy beach stretches for miles in each direction. We spend the entire afternoon building sandcastles, swimming, and lying in the sun. We enjoy swimming so much that Czar purchases a plastic pool for the front yard. It is approximately a foot and a half deep and at least eight feet across. He fills it with warm water from the hose. The neighborhood boys must take turns coming over to play because there are too many of them. Only one little girl comes, and she also has five brothers. Czar often squirts water at us from the hose to cool us off, and we splash around in the pool for hours. I make good use of my ducky swimsuit wearing it every day. Whenever Czar leaves us alone, the girl grabs the hose and sticks it between her legs squirting water like it is coming out of an earthworm. She knows lots about earthworms. I try the hose trick too, and then we roll around in the pool laughing.

Small Sis's fifteenth birthday comes, and we bake her a chocolate cake with lemon pudding filling and chocolate fudge frosting. She is happy for a while. However, later in the day, she begins missing White Knight and cries all evening wanting to go home. I can't understand why she would ever want to leave. We have use of the television, bathtub, canal, swimming pool, and hose. I couldn't care less if I ever went back home. Big Sis is also a good cook, and the food is better out east. I even look forward to grocery shopping with her. She always lets me pull the wagon to the store. As we walk up and down the aisles, she tells me what she wants; and I load up the cart. Once the groceries are paid for, we hoist the brown bags onto the wagon and haul them home. I help her put them away in the cupboards. I don't even mind taking out the trash and dropping it into the metal cans that we move to the front of the house on garbage day. Everything is new to me, and I want to spend as much time at the home of the Czars as possible.

Near the end of our visit, Czar treats us to a day at an amusement park with its rides and games sprawling out along a sandy white beach. The main attraction is the huge roller coaster. After plenty of coaxing, he convinces Small Sis to ride it with him. She screams from the time their car streaks down the highest peak at the beginning of the ride to the last dip and curve of it. Then he teases her about it all the way home. However, the highlight of our vacation is a trip to the falls approximately twenty minutes away from their house. The grounds are crowded with vehicles and people. We stand at the railing from which we enjoy an unrestricted view of the river and falls. The water crashes down with a continuous roar filling the air with a thick mist. I turn away from the railing for a moment, and my attention focuses on a woman carrying a baby and leading a little boy by the hand. I can't believe how dark their skin is, and more astonishing is the fact that the palms of their hands and soles of their feet are pink. The woman doesn't resemble Aunt Jemima on the pancake mix box. She is tall and skinny. Her hair is tied back with a bright yellow ribbon that matches her long cotton frock. The baby is dressed in a white romper. Seeing the baby makes me recall the day I decided what I would ask for in my letter to Santa. I had settled on two possibilities, Pumpkinhead or a doll that looked very much like the baby in its mother's arms. In the end, I chose Pumpkinhead because he was more "Christmasy". I also see Chinese people for the first time. I heard that their skin is yellow but don't think it is any different from mine. I notice that their eyes are almond-shaped like those of the Chinese fisherman in pictures illustrating the story about cormorants in one of the books Granny read to me.

After everyone has seen enough of the water, we take a walk in the gardens. The center of a field, with perfectly manicured grass, features a large clock designed with flowers and surrounded by flowerbeds containing many varieties of beautiful blossoms. To my surprise, Czar hands me two one-dollar bills to spend in the souvenir shop. I carefully study every item on the shelves. My choice is a tiny blue lantern with a matching plate behind it. Each is clasped in a wooden holder decorated with a painting of the falls. The lamp has a wick that can burn lantern or perfume oil. On the way out, we stop at the ice cream counter and then decide to take one more trek to the falls for a last look.

Way down below us, we watch the ferry crowded with people dressed in bright yellow raincoats taking part in a tour behind the surging water of the falls. The day was a very special one for me —an unforgettable experience for a girl from the end of the line. Late that night, I wrap the lantern in tissue paper and place it in Frizzy's suitcase, which I had already begun packing for the trip home.

The dreaded day of our departure is soon a reality. My sister and her whole family come to see us off at the station. After several minutes of crying and hugging, we are back on the train. I feel fine for a while but experience nausea after the first day and suffer from motion sickness for the remainder of the journey.

When we return home, Mom still has $1.50 of the $2.75 with which we started off the trip; this, I conclude, is nothing short of a miracle. Knight took charge of the animals while we were gone. He meets us at the train station and fills us in on the news as he drives us home. Mr. Mustache died of a heart attack shortly after we left. I feel guilt and relief at the same time—guilt because I wished I wouldn't have him for a teacher so he had to die for me to get my wish, and relief because I wouldn't get a strap from him. Additional and more joyful news is that Granny is living in town. She married a man who lives near Mom's church. The purpose of her trip at Easter was to meet the future husband. I am so excited about the prospect of seeing her again but wonder how she feels about Daddy after the Easter episode and, therefore, about me.

I must talk to Johnny about my trip and about Granny. I hurry over to the big rock hoping he is still there. "Johnny, it's me. I didn't want to come home but I'm back. I wish Big Sis would have taken me with them when they moved out east."

"Hi, Little One. You know deep down, she couldn't. Your parents and sisters would never have let you go. You belong here," Johnny explains. I am so relieved to hear his voice, which reassures me that things are again back to normal.

"They aren't even rich; yet they have a TV, bathtub, inside toilets, hot and cold running water, and a furnace to keep them warm in the winter. Look at how we live. They are so much better off than we are that even their milk and bread tastes better than ours does, and I can't even imagine how really rich people live and the things they must have. It's not fair...."

"Take heed of this old saying, 'The best things in life are free'. You don't need money to be happy, but I would have to agree that it does help. Keep in mind that there are many people in this world who are worse off than you are."

"I don't think I can stand living through another winter. I hate the cold weather. Besides, there isn't even Santa to look forward to anymore. The only reason I'm glad I came back is to talk to you. I didn't see any big rocks there, except for at the falls. I'm so happy Granny is back. I want to visit her, but I'm not sure how she feels about me because of what happened with Daddy."

"Don't worry. You are special to her and always will be. She's forgiven your daddy and forgotten about what happened a long time ago," he concludes. Johnny eases my fears somewhat, and I am grateful to him for that.

33

School will be starting again in a couple of days. We must buy our own texts from students who passed to the next grade or from the grocery store that stocked new and used books. I have all of my books, except for one, so I head to the store to find it and buy the last copy. As I leave the store, I spot Granny walking with her new husband in the distance. They enter their yard, and I decide to follow them. From the shadows, I watch as they disappear into the house through the back door. I wait for a few moments and then climb the steps. I am still uncertain about how she will feel about seeing me. After three aborted attempts, I tap gently on the door. Then Granny appears at the screen. I breathe a sigh of relief when she smiles, opens the door, and holds out her arms to hug me. Johnny is right again. She introduces me to her husband. "You can call him 'Gramps'," she says with a grin as she touches his arm. He is much shorter than Granny but wears trifocals like hers. "See, I promised you I would come back; and here I am," she exclaims. "Now tell me about your trip."

"I had so much fun. I watched television and went swimming. Mom sewed me a bathing suit. I also saw a roller coaster. We went to the falls and I saw Negro and Chinese people. I didn't want to stare at them, but there aren't any around here."

"It's natural for people to be suspicious and curious about those who are different from them. When white people enter the jungle, the natives want to touch their fair skin and hair. The natives could end up being friendly towards them or they might even kill them. There is no way to predict how they might react. I was just studying this book and contemplating about how apes and people resemble each other." I never before saw that particular book. We sit close to the table, and she begins to turn the pages illustrated with various monkeys and apes.

"I think I look like that one and a bit like that one," I marvel pointing at one and then the other.

"That's an orangutan, and the other monkey is a chimpanzee," she determines. "I agree with you that white people look the most like them." We view more pictures of the jungle animals. Many of them are hairy with faces of different colors.

"Oh, look," I squeal. "That one has a purple face. Wouldn't it be funny if I had a purple face?"

"That one has red chili pepper-shaped nose. Wouldn't it be funny if I had a nose like that," she laughs. "I think people have been around for a long time, but I don't know whether they evolved from apes or along with them. Both species seem to disappear for long periods of time and then reappear in cycles of tens of thousands of years." Granny is so clever. She always has something interesting to discuss and continues her lecture as she brews some tea. I feel all grown up when she pours me a cup. We chat more about my trip out east and about people and apes. Her husband makes the occasional comment but seems content to just listen to her speak. It is late when I get home, but nobody notices.

I am looking forward to being in Grade IV now that Mr. Mustache is gone and will be replaced by his daughter. Everyone describes her as being young, pretty, and too nice to give kids a strap every day. On the first day of school, Small Sis dresses me up in jeans with the pant legs rolled up to the middle of my calves and a sleeveless white shirt decorated with navy and red stick people. My hair has grown considerably, but I won't dare ask my mother to help me with it or she might cut it again. All summer, I practiced pulling it back into a ponytail and twisting an elastic band around it to keep it in place. I quickly secure my ponytail and coax my bangs into a curl at one side of my forehead. Then I rush to school anxious to meet my new teacher. She is not very tall with a turned-up nose and short brown hair combed back into a ducktail, the latest hairstyle. I decide to call her "Misty" for "Miss T" for "Miss Teacher". My desk is at the very back of the room so I can't see what she is wearing. The room is crowded with at least fifty students in Grades IV to VIII, the majority of them in the lower grades. In one of her first announcements, Misty holds up a V-shaped plaque adorned with a silver plate that is attached to a cherry wood frame. "This plaque is dedicated to the memory of my father. Every year, the best student, that is, in marks and behavior in our room will get his or her name engraved on it," she explains with her voice full of emotion. It occurs to me that she must be missing her dad. The first couple of weeks of school fly by. Misty is a wonderful teacher with an unusual way of teaching that almost tricks us into learning. Her specialties are art and music. At first, I find it difficult to believe that music can be written down on paper; but, after several of her lessons, I am convinced.

A friend of my dad's asks Mom if his niece can stay at our place to attend school until Christmas, when her parents plan to be settled in the big city. There is no where else for her to go so, of course, Mom takes her in. She is tall for age twelve; she is in my grade because she failed several times. She wears glasses with thick lenses and square, light-colored frames. Her dark blonde shoulder-length hair is parted in the middle and curls under at the ends. She is very quiet and stays in the bedroom at the kitchen entrance. Small Sis and I have moved into the Main Street Bedroom and sleep together in the double bed. I name the new girl "Mattie," a short form for her long Ukrainian surname. She doesn't do very well in our first tests, especially in social studies and science. After some encouragement from us, she becomes more friendly and talkative, admitting that she never does homework and that her study habits are poor. Within weeks, we move a cot into our room for her. We spend the evenings doing our homework and studying together. Her marks begin to improve, and she is more than pleased. On extra cold nights, she crawls into bed with us. We study, chat, and laugh late into the night and rise early to study some more.

34

In November, Mom buys an electric cook stove, which is a momentous occasion in our lives. It is big, white, and shiny with black knobs on the top back, four coiled elements, and a glass window in the oven door. Jigger-r-r-ram moved his radio repair business into his own shop so the stove is set up in the back of the store close to the electrical box. Mom hires a carpenter to set up a partition with two doorways about one third of the way from the rear wall of the store to form a kitchen. He builds cupboards and installs a double stainless steel sink under the new window that faces the hotel. We still have no running water, but now water carried from the town well or rain barrel can easily be heated in a kettle on the electric stove. The wood-burning heater remains in its spot next to the new stove. Daddy removes the cook stove from the old kitchen and replaces it with an oil-burning heater. The old kitchen became the living room and the living room a bedroom. Eventually, Mom orders a refrigerator, freezer, and wringer washing machine from the catalogue through her budget plan.

One night, Mom forgot to turn off the large element on the stove. I happened to be up late, noticed it because it was red hot, and switched it off. From that moment on, along with securing the doors, I took it upon myself to inspect the stove before going to bed. For some reason, I decide I also must check the boxes under the counters, too, just in case some drunk wandered into the house and hid in one of them. With the wooden yardstick, I whack the boxes. Checking and whacking becomes a nightly ritual, and I can't fall asleep unless I do it. At least, I don't have to worry about the troll because three old men moved in with him upstairs. They needed board and room because their families wouldn't care for them; but, of course, Mom would. She needed the money and receives a portion of their pension checks. I call them as the "Three Stooges" although I would never admit it out loud—old people must be respected. I might have to respect them, but I don't have to like them. They do nothing to make them likable. They are always smoking, coughing, spitting, and complaining. Thank goodness, they will be shipped off to the old folks' home in the spring.

We aren't looking forward to Christmas because that is when Mattie must leave. When she drives off with her parents, we all weep. Preparing for Christmas takes our minds off missing her. Small Sis's present from Knight is an engagement ring. She is afraid to tell Mom, but we decide there is nothing she can do about it anyway. On Christmas morning, we huddle under the covers admiring the ring. It came in a delicate silver box in the shape of two hearts joined together side by side. The interior is lined with red velvet and has an empty slot for the wedding ring. They plan to marry in the summer after she turns sixteen. I don't know how she could choose to quit school and get married so young. She probably made up her mind that marriage and a family were what she wanted long ago, when she first saw Knight. We drive to Med Sis's later in the day for turkey and trimmings and celebrate after Knight and my sister announce their engagement. My present from Med Sis is a round glass trinket-saver. The top is adorned with a beautiful swan formed of transparent glass with its back hollowed out to hold a cylindrical bottle of cologne.

After Christmas, temperatures plummet. I fear that the new burner will somehow quit working or run out of fuel, and, as a result, we'll freeze to death in our sleep. Mom must have been thinking the same thing because she orders more oil. It has to be carried into the house in a metal container; the tank on the burner is filled by hand. I watch from the side window of the Main Street Bedroom as the truck begins to back into our yard to deliver our barrel of oil. There is a strong possibility that it will get stuck in the deep snow before making it to the shack where the barrels are stored, even though its wheels are fitted with enormous chains to improve traction. The young driver shifts the truck back and forth several times in order to forge its own path through the drifts. He waves and grins at me through the frosty windshield as he successfully backs all the way into our yard. It appears as though he is showing off for me. I cheer anyway when I run to the back door and watch him triumphantly roll the barrel into the shack. Then he hops back into the truck, which follows its tracks back onto Main Street and disappears into the blowing snow.

The evenings are long and time passes slowly. I am too big for my two-wheeled trike and write to Daddy reminding him that I want a bicycle, more than anything else, for my birthday. I don't dare shoot rubber rings through the stairwell window fearing I might run into one of the stooges when retrieving the rings. Instead of participating in my old games, I pin curl my hair every night. Sleeping with bobby pins sticking into my scalp is not very comfortable, but I like how my hair looks the next day. I also read a lot, mainly because I must write book reports for Misty. One Saturday, I spend all afternoon drafting a rough copy of a report on newsprint. All I am required to do is regurgitate what happens in the book in my own words and write the final copy on a sheet of foolscap that was allotted in class. Late Sunday evening, I decide to gather up my books and papers for school. In the process, I pick up my book report and gasp in shock when I discover that the bottom-third of my sheet of foolscap is ripped off and missing. I had written on both sides to the bottom of the sheet. In a flash, I realize what happened.

One of the Three Stooges, and I know which one, ripped off the strip of paper, rolled it up, stuck it in the bottom damper of the heater, and used the flame to light a cigarette instead of using one of his own matches. I am furious. As I approach him, he stands there looking at me with his beady eyes, one on each side of his hooked nose, acting as if he has done nothing wrong. I want to cram that cigarette down his throat, but Mom stops me. I break down in tears. After I calm down, she helps me cut a piece of paper to fit the foolscap. I rewrite the missing lines of the report, tape the two pieces together, and hand it in to Misty the next day. Concerns that I might be in trouble because of the torn paper prove to be unfounded, as nothing comes of it.

All too soon, Misty makes the sad announcement that she will be leaving the middle of February. On Valentine's Day, at our school party, she decides to award the plaque in memory of her father to the best student for the first time. To my surprise, she calls my name and invites me up to the front of the class. I am stunned and thrilled at the same time and float to the front of the room like a cloud. As she shakes my hand, I see my name engraved near the top of the plaque under her dad's. Ironically, she chose me unaware of how afraid I was of her father and how guilty I felt when he died. Misty introduces us to our new teacher, a young woman, who also seems very nice; but, in my mind, will have a hard time filling Misty's shoes. I am sad to see her go but happy to see two of the stooges leave before Easter. The old man with the beady eyes stays on.

35

For my birthday, Daddy gives me a bike, my beautiful Glider, with dark blue fenders. One of the mechanics at the garage helped him put it together. Now I am riding it, moving like the wind, while trying to avoid the roughest bumps in the graveled road behind our property. I head out of town and stop for a rest beyond the tracks, beside a freshly-cultivated field. After propping up my bike with the kickstand, I sit in the tall grass beside a shallow ditch. I notice a baby killdeer running along the furrows on its long skinny legs. Its snowy white delicately-feathered breast puffs out as it calls for its mother. I jump across the ditch and run after it, never expecting to catch it; but I do. It is the cutest thing, cuter than the baby chicks and ducklings we hatched. I must show it off to Daddy and Small Sis. I cup it in my hands and make a beeline for my bike. My plan is to place it in my pocket while I drive home. Alas, my foot strikes a jagged rock in the soft soil causing my ankle to twist. As a result, I lose my balance and fall forward in slow motion. I hold out my left hand to block my fall in order to protect the baby. After lying there for only seconds, I frantically check to see if it is okay. To my horror, the bird is lifeless—its neck broken from being caught between my fingers and the force of my fall. I don't pray for it. Praying won't bring it back to life. Why did God allow this to happen? I stroke its tiny body as my own becomes shell-shocked with guilt. I sob out loud as I stumble back to the edge of the field. Using a sharp rock, I scrape a shallow hole in the ground, place the baby bird gently in the grave, cover it with some wild flowers, and bury it with dirt and a mound of small rocks. My tear-filled eyes scan the sky, but the mother killdeer is nowhere to be seen. I must confess to Johnny. I guide my bike into the yard as close as possible to the big rock. "Oh, Johnny. I feel so awful. I should have left the little killdeer alone. I hate myself," I sob as I beat at my body with my fists.

"Don't be so hard on yourself. The mother abandoned that baby because there was something physically wrong with it. You would never have caught it, if it were healthy. You're right about leaving nature alone though—that is the true way to love nature," explains Johnny in an attempt to console me. Silence follows our brief conversation. I don't feel any better after confessing to Johnny and am prepared to accept my self-inflicted punishment. For years, I dedicated Christmas day to the remembrance of the reindeer with it eyes frozen open. Now my birthday will become a day to mourn the baby killdeer.

The passing of time allows me to begin to accept what I did to the baby bird. My thoughts turn to a happier event, the upcoming wedding of Small Sis and Knight. Mom is working again on the gowns she sewed for Med Sis's wedding. She alters the design by adding two strips of gathered netting approximately three inches wide on the skirts and fashioning sleeveless boleros with small pointed collars to wear with them. I am happy to have an excuse to wear my mine again. It fits fine even though I have grown taller in the two years since Med Sis's wedding. We rejoice in the news that Big Sis and her three sons plan to attend the wedding but will be traveling by train this time. She really must want to come, I think, reliving the sickness I experienced on the train. Hopefully, none of the boys would get it. Without a doubt, the trip would be worse for all of them if she got it.

Practice for Field Day is again in progress. The captain of the baseball team is trying to recruit a rookie to complete his team. The ages of the players on the team must add up to or below a certain sum. His team has a couple of older players so he is looking for somebody good and young enough to meet the requirements. He saw me play ball and knows I prefer to catch with my bare hands. One recess, as he walks with me to the ball diamond, he squints at me through his pop-bottle glasses and asks if I would be interested in playing for his team. Of course I was, so he promised to teach me to catch with a glove. Now I have something else to practice and keep at it for hours. I bounce the sponge ball off the side of the shack and soon catch it in my gloved hand with confidence. I miss not having Frenchie around to give me advice. He was a good ball player. Our team makes it to the finals in the ball tournament on Field Day. It is my turn to bat in the last inning, and the captain wants me to try for a walk. I am small; and the pitcher throws four high ones in a row allowing me to walk to first, after which, I advance to second. Then the captain gets a hit, and I score what proves to be the winning run. We go on to win the tournament, and the captain is forever indebted to me.

That year's summer holiday turns out to be one of my best. Small Sis and Knight often take me to the lake. My swimming improves, and I even master floating on my back. I also spend time at Med Sis's. She is pregnant and getting big because the baby is due in September. The farmyard is shaping up. Med Sis is a hard worker; she moves out most of the junk and plants a lot of flowers. She also made improvements in the house. My job is to polish furniture. My invention, a pointed stick covered with the dust rag, becomes my best friend as I attack dust embedded in the deeply carved crevices of the antique furniture. As I work, I sing a song derived from my motto: I must do my best in order to have no regrets in the future. My reward is the fun I have playing board games every night.

A week before the wedding, Big Sis and the three Czars arrive. Knight meets them at the train station. The two older boys have grown as much as I have. I avoid them in an attempt to stay out of trouble. The baby Czar is cute, blonde, and has just turned one year old. I keep away when he has his bath.

Two days before the wedding, my happy holiday comes to a halt when I am plagued with a toothache. I suffer all night; next day my cheek begins to swell. The old man with the beady eyes talks Daddy into using one of his remedies. He takes a gallon of vinegar from the kitchen cupboard and orders Daddy to fetch the thick blanket from the cubbyhole. Then they proceed to stack some bricks in the back yard, arranging them so that dry twigs and paper can be stuffed underneath. The old man strikes a match and ignites the paper. The act rekindles the memory of my burnt book report, and I flinch in anticipation. When the bricks become hot enough and the fire diminishes, he pours on the vinegar and spreads the blanket over top to capture the fumes. They grab me and thrust my head under the blanket urging me to breathe in. I struggle to get away but am too weak from hours of suffering and lack of sleep. The old man pushes my head in further. A failed attempt to keep my mouth and eyes closed as tightly as possible and trying not to breathe places my life in jeopardy. Then, like a miracle, I hear Big Sis's voice as she tries to beat them off. "You're going to kill her," she screams as she begins to panic. With her help, I manage to break away from them, gasping for air and fighting to regain my eyesight. "We're taking her to see a doctor right now," she vows.

Daddy arranges for one of the neighbors to drive Mom, him, and me to see the doctor. Mom is worried. I sleep most of the way in the back seat with my head in her lap. The doctor is a tall thin man with a narrow face and gray brush cut. He examines me closely giving me a complete physical. His diagnosis is that I have an abscessed tooth that must be removed. The freezing provides me with instant relief from the pain. He yanks the tooth back and forth and shows me the sacks on the root as he holds it up the air with a pair of long-nosed pliers. He tells Mom that I am too thin and asks her if I have ever had rheumatic fever. She is sure I didn't but mentions that I often ran high temperatures when I was little. On the way home, Mom smiles when I inform her that I am hungry for canned meat and fried potatoes—a sure sign that I am feeling better. At that point, our thoughts turn from my tooth to the wedding, which is only hours away. After spending the afternoon at the hospital with me, Mom is running late with the food preparations. With the help of my sisters, everything is under control by midnight.

Small Sis had ordered her wedding gown from the catalogue. After my sisters help her into the dress, we all stand back and admire it when she makes her entrance into the living room. She looks like a princess. The gown has a fitted lace bodice with spaghetti straps. The floor-length skirt that flares out from the waist features lace on the top half and gathered netting at the bottom. The lace and netting are divided by a zigzagging band of sequins. She puts on a matching long-sleeved bolero with a small collar and then a long veil with a sequined tiara to complete the ensemble.

After a short ceremony at the United Church, the wedding party heads for the big town where studio portraits are taken and then drives all the way back for supper at the hall beside Mom's church. Everyone is having a good time dancing in the hall and eating in the kitchen area. I am standing by Daddy and Med Sis when two police officers enter the kitchen through the side door. They proceed to smell the liquor bottles on the table. The second officer looks familiar, and my stomach begins to churn when I realize he is the one who took Daddy away the night of the Easter incident. The look on his face tells me that he recognized us at the same time. Daddy and Med Sis hurry over to speak to him, and I follow. Then Small Sis and Knight join us. The officer apologizes for crashing the wedding, but a complaint that home-brew would be served had been filed. Knight suspects that one of his neighbors is the culprit, being jealous of their marriage, obsessed with the idea that Small Sis should have married HER brother. The police officers try not to disrupt the party but have no choice other than to order that it must be shut down at midnight. I am relieved at the decision as I feared that somebody else might be dragged away. The celebration continues until the last minute. Small Sis and Knight leave directly from the hall for their honeymoon.

As I lie in bed, I lament the fact that Small Sis will be moving away to Knight's farm and won't be living at home any more. At least she wouldn't have her in-laws around, as they are retired and living out east. I never found out if home-brew was served at supper, and I don't really care. So much has happened in the past twenty-four hours that I forgot about the vinegar incident. As I run my tongue along the packing in my gum, I contemplate my bleak future. I dread being all alone with my sisters gone. For now, I am comforted by the fact that Big Sis will be around almost until school starts.

The last Sunday before Big Sis and her family are to leave, we make a trip into the country to visit relatives who own a thriving farm. Hoping to find animals besides the two collie-crosses that greet me with wagging tails and sniffing noses, I run off to inspect the barn. The dogs follow me to the barn, which is much larger than ours. Inside, it's very clean and empty, filling me with an eerie feeling. The cows are obviously in the pasture. As I walk back toward the house, I hear voices. Fortunately, I overhear part of the conversation of a group of boys made up of relatives and a couple of their friends from the farms nearby. Czar I is also with them. They are planning to lure me to the barn, and there they will "fix" me. I hurry to the kitchen entrance without being seen and play with the dogs pretending to be unaware of the scheme as two of the boys approach me.

"Come and play hide-and-go-seek at the barn," hollers the dark-haired boy.

"Okay, I'll come and look for you after I count to five hundred," I call. They turn and snicker as they head for the barn. I snicker too because I would never be stupid enough to enter that barn knowing what I know. If anything happened to me, I'd be the one to blame because boys can do no wrong. I sit on a chair in the kitchen and straighten out the red, white, and black plaid taffeta skirt of my dress with the palms of my hands as I wait. Mom ordered it for me from the catalogue when I told her I liked it. The top has puffy short sleeves and two rows of lace on either side of a row of black buttons with tiny rhinestones in their centers. The flared skirt rustles when I walk. I tap the toes of my black patent shoes gently on the floor as I count. Instead of venturing outside, I help my aunt set the wooden table in the dining room. The kitchen table is already set for the boys. When they come in to eat, they ask me why I didn't come to the barn to find them, complaining that they waited in their dumb hiding spots forever. I smile my sweetest innocent smile and remain silent. I sit far away from them beside Mom in the dining room to feast on my perogies and pickled beets with horseradish.

36

It is a sad day when Big Sis leaves, but two days later my spirits rise when the old man with the beady eyes moves to an old folk's home. At least I don't have to worry about his trying to kill me again. As it turns out, I won't be left on my own without Small Sis after all, because three students from the farm will be staying at our place to attend high school. I am anxious to meet them when they arrive the evening before school starts. The girl is a relative of Mom's first husband and will be in Grade X. She roomed by herself in town the previous year. She is fairly tall and wears glasses. Her short brown hair is tightly permed and parted in the middle. She refers to me as her cousin. I'm really not but I call her "Kuz" anyway.

One of the two boys is also a relative of Mom's first husband. His thick blonde hair is parted on the side and combed back. He is very shy and speaks in a soft voice. The other boy is also blonde and very quiet. The two are so much alike they could easily be mistaken for twins. They carry their belongings upstairs, and I can't help smiling because, like the stooges, they won't realize that they are sleeping with the troll.

Kuz moves her luggage, along with a typewriter and chalkboard, into the Main Street Bedroom. She is planning to enroll in a commercial course after Grade XI and wants to practice her typing, and I am also able to continue with mine.

The first days of school pass without incident. In the evenings, the boy who is Mom's relative strums his guitar and sings while we all gather around to listen. I name him "Guitar Boy." As for Kuz, most of her studying is done on the blackboard, so Mom and I fall asleep in the back bedroom every night listening to the tapping of her keys or the tapping of her chalk.

Med Sis's baby boy is born in September. He is tiny with fair curly hair, and I christen him "Duke I." She is now too busy with the baby and the farm to come and pick me up on weekends. I miss her but must admit that I am enjoying the company of the high school students staying at our place.

One day, a young pup follows me home from school. He is the typical farm dog with dark brown coat and light brown dots above his eyes. Some farmer probably dropped him off in town hoping that someone like me would adopt him. I decide to keep him, and Mom doesn't seem to mind. Besides, Smoky is getting old and spends most of his time lying by the back door in the kitchen. The new members of our family bring us dairy products, eggs, and other food from the farm as partial payment for their board and room so there is plenty of milk and leftovers for the pup. After his first meal, he flips onto his back with his paws in the air. I still haven't decided on a name for him. As I scratch his round tummy, it occurs to me that I should dub him "Tubby." He sleeps in the big shack on some old quilts and jackets. When the nights are too cold, he sleeps in the house beside Smoky.

A new cat moved into the barn. Mom is pleased because she is a mouse catcher. Nancy occasionally appears like a witch and slinks around the house for a few minutes before bolting out the door. She still isn't very popular. The new cat has long soft fur with patches of brown and orange on a white background. I name her "Fluffy." When I finally manage to coax her into the house, I discover that she is friendly, not like Nancy. Soon she begins to jump up onto my lap to enjoy some petting.

The Christmas parcel from Big Sis arrives early. It contains a wrapped gift for me. I place it under the tree that Kuz and I decorated before she went home for the holiday. At least, I know for certain that I will have something to open. I feel so alone when I wake up on Christmas morning. I miss Mattie, my sisters, and even the high school kids. Surprisingly, opening my present, a black lacquered jewelry box, changes my day for the better. The outside of the lid features a hand-painted picture of a girl wearing a blue gown. Her skin is a bright white and starkly contrasts with her black hair arranged in fancy buns held in place with a golden ornament. She is wearing red sandals on her bright white feet and stands under a tree bearing white blossoms. In the distance, a red house with a strangely shaped roof nestles in the foothills of a gray mountain. The front of the box is decorated with a painted arrangement of light blue flowers and slender leaves under a golden two-piece clasp. I open it slowly and am greeted by music—a gentle tinkling melody that brings tears to my eyes. A tiny ballerina wearing a netted skirt attached to a strapless top twirls around and around in front of three vertical mirrors. The two side mirrors are tilted creating the illusion of three ballerinas dancing. The interior is lined with red velveteen. When the music stops, the ballerina also ceases to dance. As I close the lid, I notice a tiny key in the back. I wind it carefully and play the music over and over again watching the ballerina and her mirror partners dance. Later in the day, I move Granny's combs into the jewelry box. I place it on a stand near Mom's bed and rearrange my treasures.

Granny and Gramps are invited for Christmas supper. Daddy is home, but I don't have to worry about a confrontation. He made his apologies to her for the Easter incident after she moved back into town. The fact that they are friends again is very comforting, because I care so much for both of them. Clutching the music box, I meet Granny and Gramps at the door; I can hardly wait for her to remove her coat. When she sits down on the couch, I set the box on her lap and lean so close to her that I can smell the ointment that she is obviously still using. She examines it closely, turning it from side to side with her long fingers. "This is a painting of a geisha girl, a young Japanese woman, who sings and dances for men," she explains as she opens the lid. I can tell that she recognizes the melody from the expression on her face. She begins to sing to the music, "It was fascination; I know, ta, da, da, da.... I've forgotten the words," she remarks apologetically. "I see my combs, I mean, your combs in here. I knew you would take good care of them."

"I wore them often when you were gone, and I still wear them whenever I am sad because they seem to bring me joy. They are very special to me, and now I have a special place in which to store them," I reply. Then our company begins to arrive. Med Sis comes in with the new baby, Duke, her in-laws, and Duke's brother. Small Sis and Knight are right behind them. Everyone fusses over Baby Duke. Small Sis looks different to me, and I suspect she might be pregnant. Sure enough, they announce that she is expecting the end of May. Big Sis is also pregnant again and due in April. Our family is growing by leaps and bounds. We enjoy supper and visit until midnight because we don't get together very often any more. When everyone has left, I listen to the music box and fall asleep thinking about the reindeer with its eyes frozen open.

37

In the winter months, we play outdoor soccer at recess because we have no gym. We call it "football". My baseball captain picks me, the first of the girls, to be on his team. The captain of the other team is a rugged, hard-nosed player. I often play forward but prefer to be in the goal, even though

I'm often kicked in the shins or hit in the face with the ball. The cold weather clearly intensifies the pain of a smack in the face instead of dulling it. When the end of the season draws to a close, each of our two teams has the same number of points. The outcome of a tie-breaking game will determine the winner. This is serious business, and my captain orders me to play forward. Near the end of the scoreless game, I check the opposing captain and pass the ball to mine, who scores on a breakaway. He dashes over to me after the game and slaps me on the back. "If it weren't for you, we wouldn't have won!" he guffaws.

Winter seems to last forever, but Easter finally arrives. Daddy is home again. The morning after returning, he heads to the corner store to catch up on the news. The gossips inform him that Old Man Click is in the hospital. It is an accepted fact that whenever anybody his age is admitted to the hospital they never come back. Therefore, Daddy is concerned and catches a ride with Knight to visit him. When he comes home in the evening, it is snowing again. We sit down for a late meal. Daddy tells us with a grin that the old man is barely alive but still singing. Even while he was at Old Man Click's bedside, the nurses continued to draw blood for testing. Daddy describes it as being a dark brown color, resembling tar. Meowing at the kitchen door interrupts our supper. Daddy opens it and in darts Fluffy, who disappears upstairs. As soon as he sits down, she is back at the door wanting out. A few moments later, there is meowing at the door again. Daddy is greeted again by Fluffy. This time we notice she has a kitten in her mouth and is, without a doubt, seeking shelter for her babies from the cold. When she is done, there are six kittens in the far corner of the closet where she made a bed in a woolly coat that had fallen off a hanger.

Old Man Click died during Easter break. Daddy is

visibly upset when he hears the news and whispers, "Die, die once. Happy, the day you born. Happy, the day you die," in an attempt to comfort himself. Petunia spends most of the time before his funeral at our place. She sits on a kitchen chair, rocks back and forth for hours, and then dozes off. Within minutes, she awakens with a start, pulls up her skirt, removes a handkerchief from the top of her brown stocking, and undoes the knots. Inside the handkerchief are coins that she counts. Then she ties the coins back up in the handkerchief, rolls them back up in the top of her stocking, and resumes her rocking back and forth. She repeats the process numerous times during each visit.

Several nights in a row, I dream about Old Man Click buried in the wooden coffin he built for himself and now I'm afraid to go to bed. I decide to discuss my dreams with Granny. She isn't getting out much because the streets are still slippery. After taking one look at me, she asks,

"What's wrong? You look so tired."

"Granny, I've been dreaming about Old Man Click. I worry about him. Is he is in heaven or hell?"

"Well, before too long, I may end up in one of those places; or maybe not. I wonder what would happen if he and I tried to get into heaven at the same time. I can just picture Saint Peter and Saint Paul at the gate. They are men, and men adore Old Man Click so they would let him in. He'd have a better chance of getting past them than I would, but I just can't picture him running around in a white dress when he'd rather wear his leather pants. The fact that Paul is sitting at the front gate, deciding who to let in and who to keep out, bothers me. I feel sure that conditions in heaven for women will be the same as they are here on earth.

"You know that my parents were staunch Christians whose faith was based on a few 'good' passages from the Bible. As a youngster, I was led to believe what they believed and never questioned our religion. Since I recently finished reading the Bible in its entirety, at this late stage in my life, my faith has crumbled; but I am okay with that. In the process, I have become Paul's nemesis as, I believe, all women should be. Paul is responsible for negative messages regarding women in the Bible that obsesses about virginity and female submission, but I must admit that it also obsesses about circumcision and money."

Granny reaches for her notes and her Bible and continues, "Before I go any further, I want to tell you about Paul; but first, I'm going to check the dictionary to see if it says anything about him. This Webster's Dictionary belongs to Gramps and has extra large print." She flips through the pages and continues, "Yes, here he is, 'in the Bible, a Jew of Tarsus; apostle of Christianity to the Gentiles; originally called Saul; also Saint Paul'." Then she explains, "A Gentile is any person who is not a Jew. I'm going to read to you from my notes about Paul. Acts 9, Saul's Conversion and Saul in Damascus and Jerusalem, describes how Paul becomes an apostle of Jesus. Paul is on his way to Damascus to take the followers of Jesus as prisoners. He is surrounded and blinded by a flash of light from heaven and is asked by a voice, identified as belonging to Jesus, why Saul has persecuted him. After instructions from Jesus, Paul is taken to Straight Street in Damascus where Ananias places his hands on Saul who is then filled with the Holy Spirit. The man restores his sight and baptizes him because he has been chosen by God to carry Jesus' name before the Gentiles. After spending several days with the disciples, he preaches in the synagogues that Jesus is the son of God and proves to the Jews that Jesus is the Christ." Granny pauses for a moment and comments, "There is no explanation given of how he proved it. Obviously he didn't because, to this day, Jews don't believe that Jesus is the son of God. However, the

Church prospered and increased in numbers. Again, there is no explanation of how the churches were established. The disciples were first called 'Christians' in Antioch. Through the Church, God opened the faith to the Gentiles who could be saved through the grace of Jesus. Paul's task was that of testifying to the gospel of God's grace."

Granny holds up her hand and twists her wrist in a downward motion, signaling for me to make some tea. As I pour the hot water into the pot and spoon in the tea leaves, she says, "It's a good thing Gramps is gone for the afternoon because now we are free to discuss a couple of things, woman to woman." She consults the dictionary and says, "Circumcision is defined as 'the act or custom of cutting off the foreskin of human males; rejection of the sins of the flesh; spiritual purification, and acceptance of the Christian faith'." I know exactly what she means because some of my nephews are circumcised and wonder what significance cutting off the end of an earthworm can have with regard to the Church, let alone to God, other than to exclude females from being accepted by the Church. Then Granny returns to her notes and reads, "Genesis 17, The Covenant of Circumcision, delivers the facts about Abram's circumcision. He is better known as 'Abraham'. When Abram was ninety-nine years old, God appeared to him to confirm their covenant. In order to do so, Abram was to undergo circumcision, which would be the sign of the covenant; and I quote, 'For generations to come, every male among you who is eight days old must be circumcised, including those born in your household or bought with money from a foreigner', end of quote. In return, Abram's numbers would be greatly increased. However, in Galatians 5, Freedom in Christ, Paul warns, 'Mark my words. I, Paul, tell you that if you let yourselves be circumcised, Christ will be of no value to you'. He continues stating, 'For in Christ Jesus neither circumcision nor uncircumcision has any value. The only thing that counts is faith expressing itself through love'." Then Granny adds, "And, thus, Paul opened the door of the Church to the Gentiles."

Granny sips on some tea taking a break as she examines her notes more closely. After a few minutes of silence, the lesson resumes. "I want to focus on the matter of money and Paul in the Church. In 2 Corinthians 2, Ministers of the New Covenant, Paul claims, 'Unlike so many, we do not peddle the word of God for profit.' However, in 1 Corinthians 16, The Collection for God's People, Paul instructs churches about collections using the Galatian churches as an example. 'On the first day of every week, each one of you should set aside a sum of money in keeping with his income, saving it up, so that when I come no collections will have to be made'." Granny comments, "I would have to say that that was pretty convenient for good old Paul. Continuing on with Paul's saga of money, in 2 Corinthians 8, Generosity Encouraged, he used the Macedonian churches as an example rejoicing that, 'poverty welled up in rich generosity. They gave beyond their ability as much as they could so they could share in the service to the saints'."

Granny reaches for the Bible and begins skimming the pages saying, "This passage brings to mind something Jesus said. Here it is in Matthew 26, Jesus Anointed at Bethany. As a woman pours very expensive perfume on Jesus's head, the disciples question her actions suggesting that the perfume should have been sold and the money given to the poor instead. Jesus supports her actions because she did it to prepare him for burial and states, 'The poor you will always have with you, but you will not always have me...what she has done also will also be told, in memory of her'." Then Granny comments, "I consider that a disturbing and disappointing statement, coming from the son of a supposedly compassionate God." She looks at me, and I quickly nod in agreement as she reads on, " In 2 Corinthians 8, Sowing Generosity, Paul encouraged giving, 'Each man should give what he has decided in his heart to give, not reluctantly or under compulsion, for God loves a cheerful giver'." Then she adds, "And I would bet that Paul agreed with God. In I Timothy 6, Love of Money, Paul warned, 'For the love of money is a root of all kinds of evil. Some people, eager for money, have wandered from the faith and pierced themselves with grief'." Granny smiles, faces me, and asks, "Do you think Paul was really blinded by the light or was his vision blurred with dollar signs when the idea of opening the Church to uncircumcised males entered his head?"

"I side with the dollar signs," I chirp. "Saint Paul, send me some grief, please," I add. "I'll use Mom's church as an example that would make Paul smile. I can't begin to imagine how much it hoards when their priests collect money from the plate; for yearly memberships; for performing marriages, baptisms, and funerals; and also for blessing food, homes, and graves every year at very little cost to themselves—sprinkling 'blessed' water around and singing a few songs nobody understands anyway. To this day, my oldest sister has not forgotten the money on the plate, which was promised to her family by the priest, at her father's funeral. The family saw not a penny of that money. Women never forget or forgive such injustice."

"I agree," nods Granny. "And I want to move on to the topic of virginity in the Bible, which, to be sure, women have never been allowed to forget. The New Testament introduces the Holy Spirit, which I referred to before in the story of Paul's conversion. It is first introduced in the story of Jesus's birth when it is used as a means of impregnating a virgin by the name of Mary. It is also used on numerous occasions to conveniently explain away the unexplainable. No comment is made about Mary's delivery or on how she remained a virgin, which obviously must have happened, because she has since been known as the Virgin Mary. Virginity is greatly celebrated and valued in the Torah. Now I'll move on to Paul and his take on virginity, and his attempt to force women into submission. In 1 Corinthians 7:25-29, Marriage, he states, 'About virgins...if a virgin marries she has not sinned. But those who marry will face many troubles in this life, and I want to spare you this, and ...he who marries the virgin does right, but he who does not marry her does even better'." Granny pauses and continues, "I must add an interesting comment he makes about marriage to widows, the unmarried, and virgins in 1 Corinthians 7: 8-10. He states, 'It is good to stay unmarried as I am. But if they cannot control themselves, they should marry, for it is better to marry than to burn in passion'." Granny throws up her hands and comments on the comment, "Isn't that a great piece of advice to be handed down from generation to generation? In 1 Timothy 5:9-14, Advice about Elders, Widows, and Slaves, he also has advice for widows. No widow may be placed on the widows' list, 'unless she is over 60 and has been faithful to her husband and is known for good deeds such as bringing up children, showing hospitality, and washing the feet of saints'. It's better for younger widows to marry 'when their sensual desires overcome their dedication to Christ', otherwise, 'they get into the habit of being idle and going about from house to house and become gossips, busybodies, and follow Satan'."

Granny stands up for a moment, checks the clock, and continues, "This is a lot to digest, but I want to finish with Paul today. He appears to be more concerned with staying unmarried than he does about females maintaining their virginity. But, bless his heart, he knows how to hand out advice on how to control women. The first step is to tell them what they can wear and how to act, which makes them more readily acceptable of all other restrictions and rules. In 1 Corinthians 11:6-11, Propriety in Worship, Paul claims that when praying or prophesizing, 'If a woman does not cover her head, she should have her hair cut off and it is a disgrace for a woman to have her hair cut off or shaved', but 'a man ought not to cover his head, since he is the image and glory of God; but the woman is the glory of man', and 'the woman ought to have a sign of authority on her head'. In I Timothy 2:9-15, Instructions on Worship, he orders that 'women should dress modestly—no braided hair, gold, pearls or expensive cloth. She should be quiet and in full submission'.

And the list goes on, 'She must not teach or have authority over a man; she must be silent for Adam was formed first, then Eve. And Adam was not the one deceived; it was the woman who was deceived and became a sinner. But women will be saved through childbearing—if they continue in faith, love and holiness through propriety'. Granny snorts, "I must dispute the part about Adam being formed first and the status which is bestowed on men because of that honor. In the first few lines of Genesis, lies the truth. 'In the beginning God created the heavens and the earth. Now the earth was formless and empty, darkness was over the surface of the deep. And God went on, 'Let there be light.' and there was light. God saw that the light was good, and he separated the light from the darkness. According to these words, God created darkness first. And, if he didn't, then who created it?—the same entity that created the people of Nod? My point is that, if darkness were created first, its status should be superior to that of light, which is not the case, in the eyes of the Bible. I rest my case and accept the fact that I probably won't get past Saint Paul at the gate because I did not bear children."

Time is passing quickly. "I wonder what's keeping Gramps," whispers Granny with some concern. "Well, this gives us a chance to complete our lesson with a few more of Paul's messages for women. In 1 Corinthians 14:33-36, Orderly Worship, Paul commands, 'As in all the congregations of the saints, women should remain silent in the churches. They are not allowed to speak, but must remain in submission, as the Law states'." Granny interrupts Paul's instructions with the comment, "And to add insult to injury, he has the gall to add, 'If they want to inquire about something, they should ask their husbands at home; for it is disgraceful for a woman to speak in church'." Then Granny mutters, as if to herself, "I suppose Paul would consider heaven a congregation of the saints so, according to him, women wouldn't be able to speak there either. And, what about the women he advised not to marry? To whom would they address their questions, to the man in the moon? Men like Paul sure like to make up rules—for religion, law, war, and all sorts of things. They even make up rules when they play with a ball. I think they make up rules because they must be in control. What is difficult to accept is the fact that women have remained complacent with these rules for hundreds of years. Men just have to be themselves; and they'll be saved whether they are circumcised or not, thanks to Paul, whom I credit with creating the laws of the Christian church. All things considered, the best scenario for me, after I die, would be to have things just the way they were before I was born—nothing there. Wouldn't men be surprised if that happened to be case for everyone? I just couldn't see myself running around in a white dress in heaven and forcing myself to remain silent. It just wouldn't be me," she chuckles. I agree with her. When I die, I also want everything to come to an end for me.

As I prepare to leave, Granny says, "So ends our lesson for today, and so much for Paul. Amen." Then she adds, "I wonder how many Christians have looked up the word "Amen" in the dictionary. Well, I have. Amen was an ancient Egyptian god of life and reproduction. How fitting that Christians unwittingly end their prayers with the name of a pagan god. So there, Paul; now that's justice for women, because they could have just as easily used the word "Women" at the end of their prayers and, at least, wouldn't have been addressing a heathen." At that moment, Gramps enters the kitchen with a smile. When I hug Granny good-bye, I realize that I have been recruited as a nemesis of Paul and congratulate myself as I walk out of the house.

As soon as I get home, the first thing I do is look up the word, Nemesis. I have a good idea of what it means but want to see it in black and white and read, "Nemesis: in Greek mythology, the goddess of retributive justice, or vengeance." The definition is more fitting than I could ever have guessed. Then I look up the word, castration, and read, "To remove the testicles; to cut out or revise, thereby depriving of essential vigor or significance." Was Webster trying to say that women are of void of essential significance because they don't have testicles—the nerve of him? Driven by anger, I then look up the word, virgin, and read, "A woman, especially a young woman who has not had sexual intercourse," which leads me to look up the word, intercourse. The definition is, "the sexual joining of two individuals; coitus; copulation," which leads me to look up the words, coitus, which is defined as, "sexual intercourse" and, copulation, which is defined as, "a joining together; coupling." Why was Noah Webster beating around the bush? I came up with a better definition for sexual intercourse when I was seven years old recalling the earthworm incident and my words, "Guys are sticking their dinks into them," and revise the definition to, "Guys are sticking their penises into their vaginas. There, I said it for you, Noah. Then I add, "Why are most men so insecure? Is it because they can't give birth?" As I lie in bed at night, I think of Paul, no, excuse me, of Saint Paul sitting at heaven's gate. I feel I have power over him as a self-proclaimed goddess, his new nemesis, and place him in the same category as Santa Claus and the Easter Bunny. I fall asleep with a smile on my face imagining Old Man Click running around in heaven in his white dress and singing his dirty songs. Saint Paul will have his hands full trying to order him to stay out of his leather pants and to be silent.

Easter break is almost over, and classes resume tomorrow so the high school students return in the early evening. The boys go upstairs while Kuz and I chat in the kitchen. Suddenly, we hear yelling and the sound of stomping feet overhead. We don't know what to make of it. The ruckus continues, and we are about to investigate when Nancy comes ripping down the stairs with the boys at her heels. "Nancy killed two of Fluffy's kittens, and we caught her trying to kill another one," Guitar Boy hollers. They find brooms and proceed to swat at Nancy who is scrambling up the windows above the counters in the store. She is desperate to get outside and almost reaches the ceiling as she claws away at thin air. Then she slides down. Guitar Boy grabs her by the tail, and a stream of pee comes shooting out of her. "Yeow!" he yelps in surprise letting go of her in a hurry as we all break into a gale of laughter. Meanwhile, the cat escapes through the open door.

"She won't dare come back," I whisper to myself. The boys take care of the dead kittens burying them in the back yard. For some time, I suspected that Nancy might be a male because she never had kittens. Now I know the horrible truth—she had had kittens and had killed them, too. I visit the rock later needing to confide in someone about the cats. "Johnny, I feel bad about what we did to Nancy."

"Don't worry. He deserved it. She was evil. I don't know how to tell you this, but I can see a black cat that resembles Nancy. You are in the big city running along a sidewalk shoveled with high banks on either side from a heavy snowfall. You are headed for the hospital because your Daddy is dying. Your eyes are blurred with tears freezing in the wind, but you can still see the black cat running on top of the crusty snow making its way directly towards you. You want to boot it so that it doesn't cross your path, but you are unable stop it. It runs right in front of you, and you know in your heart that your daddy is gone..."

I cover my ears as I leave the rock. I don't want to hear it. Granny says that nobody lives forever. I know Daddy stands a good chance of getting into heaven because he is a man who believes in God and attends church. I recall the story he often told about a fortuneteller in the old country who predicted he will die of a terrible disease when he is seventy. In an attempt to reassure myself, I calculate the number of years he has left to live before he reaches that dreaded age and hope the world will end before then. I try to convince myself that my daddy's death will never happen.

38

One day, just before my eleventh birthday, I pick up the mail before the post office closes. I am pleased to find a letter from Big Sis in our box and assume it is a birth announcement. Mom opens the envelope and begins to read the letter to herself. She smiles commenting that the baby is another boy. As she reads on, the color drains from her face. The letter falls from her hand as she slumps into a kitchen chair. I scoop up the pages and read for myself. The news is that the baby has Down Syndrome. According to doctors, he might not walk until he is five and will never make himself understood—he could be very much an invalid. I place my arms around my mother's neck in an attempt to comfort her, and we sob together for what seems like an eternity. Finally, she rises and silently continues with her work in the kitchen while I head for the rock.

"Johnny, if God exists, why does He let something like this happen? Is this one of God's miracles? Is this the Law? I've heard it said that a baby is supposed to be a gift from God. I think about my sister and her husband. They are good, generous people who go to church. I know their lives will never be the same. This isn't fair."

"Life isn't fair. I can see them standing by the baby's crib. They cry for hours at a time looking down at him wondering what they did wrong. When he is six, you will ask your sister whether she would have had an abortion if she had known in time. She'll say, 'No.' Her answer to the question will be the same when he is eleven; but, when you ask her again when he is thirteen, her answer will be different. She will be forever changed, and Czar will never whistle again," predicts Johnny.

My mother has the difficult task of telling Small Sis the bad news. Her baby is due at the end of next month. She places her hand on top of her protruding belly and cries when she hears about her sister's baby. Mom promises to pray for everything to be okay. In my mind, praying won't make any difference. I spend my eleventh birthday thinking about the reindeer with its eyes frozen open, the baby killdeer, and the baby with Down Syndrome.

Six weeks later, Small Sis gives birth to a healthy baby boy, "Knight I." I meet them at the door when they return from the hospital eager to inspect the new arrival. He is tiny and red, and I suspect from experience that all newborn babies look like this. Mom thanks the Lord for making him normal. My sister and her son stay with us for the first week while Mom encourages her to breast-feed. Afraid to get too close, I watch from the bedroom doorway. The baby can't latch on to nurse, and my sister and her baby are both frustrated. She finally gives up and decides to bottle-feed.

After Small Sis and the baby leave for the farm, my thoughts focus on Field Day. I make the tabloid team again, and all of our members do so well that we end up in first place. I also win the best student award, and my name appears on Misty's plaque for a second time. I must admit that I am feeling better. Walking home on the last day of school, I find it strange that Tubby doesn't come to greet me when I enter the back yard. I call for him around the house and barn and in the bower, but he doesn't come bounding out like he usually does. I meet my mother in the kitchen.

"Mom," I ask, "Have you seen Tubby?"

"I didn't want to have to tell you this, but I heard a shot this morning," she replies with concern.

"No, NO," I wail as she hugs me and tells me who, she thinks, killed my Tubby. I manage to break free and run out of the house. "I hate that man. He's the fat businessman who walks his sleek black Labs across Main Street several times a day. I hate him now just as much as I hate the storekeeper, who took the cleaning products. He thinks he can do anything because he has money. He'll be one of the men in heaven for sure. Let him run around in his white dress. I don't want to be there if he's there," I sob.

Spending time at my sisters' farms over the summer helps me deal with the pain of losing Tubby. I learn a lot about baby boys during my visits—how to hold, bottle-feed, burp, bathe, and diaper them. I change them quickly so I don't have to look at their earthworms. Wouldn't it be nice to secure their poop in the diaper, swing it around, and let it fly? Since that is not possible, I help my sisters with the diapers. Small Sis scrubs them on a washboard outside using water from the rain barrel. Then we dispose of the wash and rinse water with each of us grabbing one handle of the galvanized tub and dumping it behind the toilet. I don't mind hanging the diapers on the line. On rainy days, we hang them all over the house to dry.

I prefer baby-sitting to working in the garden. I hate the feel of the dry soil under my fingernails and the extreme heat of the sun beating down on my skin. I dislike bending over to pull weeds and pick rocks even more. Then there are the mosquitoes and bulldog flies, which constantly attack any exposed flesh. However, whenever I do look after the babies, my sisters enjoy a much-needed break away from them and some time to themselves, even if it means slaving in the garden. I also help them with farm and household chores, preparing meals, and washing stacks of dishes.

I acquire plenty of experience over the summer so I know how to straighten out our house when I return home. After mopping the wooden floorboards in the store several times, I discover that scrubbing them on my hands and knees achieves better results, although it is hard work. The high school students return along with Kuz's younger sister, who also arranged to stay with us. She shares the Main Street Bedroom with her sister. Being back in school is a welcomed change because I have had enough of babies, for a while, anyway. I miss the company of old people and visit Granny and Gramps as often as possible.

39

In the fall, several church bazaars and teas are held at our place. Crafts and baking are arranged on the display table, and card tables and chairs are set up beside it for customers to eat lunch. I am assigned the job of cleaning up, which is nothing new. While I am washing dishes at the sink after one particular bazaar, I sense that one of the ladies from Mom's church is watching me. After glancing at her sideways, I am repulsed by vibrations emanating from her eyes and instinctively decide she is trying to put a curse on me. I quickly turn my eyes away and don't dare look back. When she leaves, I finish the dishes, sweep the floor covered with mud tracked in by the people who attended the fundraiser, and scrub it. Then I begin to feel nauseated and barely make it to the slop pail in time. I gag and heave repeatedly catching Mom's attention. "What's wrong?" she asks in an alarmed voice.

"One of the women from our church kind of looked at me funny, and I think it made me sick," I explain.

"'Tebah oreekla'," she whispers the Ukrainian words rolling the "r." "That happens when somebody is jealous, usually of a young girl, and casts a spell on her with a bad look making her sick like you are. There is a cure some old ladies in the Ukraine used to make the curse go away, and they passed their knowledge on to the younger people." I am taken off guard when she, obviously, begins to proceed with it. She licks her hand and swipes my forehead with it.

"Wipe it off with the bottom inside of the hem of your skirt," she commands. I do as I am told. Then she yawns noisily and pretends to spit quickly to the side three times. We repeat the entire procedure three times. The voodooism reminds me of the vinegar incident and the botched attempt to end my toothache, but this cure is so much more pleasant. Strange as it sounds, I experience Mom's remedy taking effect. I feel cured almost immediately. I don't want to acknowledge the act because it is just plain weird and try to convince myself that my feeling better is just a coincidence and that I would have gotten better without the hocus-pocus. Mom notices my perplexed reaction and quickly explains, "You know, those old women, the 'Babas,' were really proud about healing sick people in the old country."

"I believe in them now," I reply with a weak smile.

Before the snow begins to fly, I buy the last hula hoop in town. After some experimentation with movement, I control the flame-coloured circle well enough to coax it up from my ankles to my neck and slip it back down again. Besides playing with the hula hoop, I am blessed with other new activities. A vending-machine man set up a couple of games in our store, which is becoming more like a cafe with regular customers dropping in to eat. One of the games features the sport of football. The player uses a spring loaded handle to pop up silver ball into a boxed frame. The ball finds its way down through a maze of pegs. At the same time, a football player at the bottom is controlled with a lever in an attempt to catch it. The other game has targets in a glass enclosure with a big gun on the outside of it. I squeeze the trigger and begin shooting and making up my own rules as I fire. I acquire 50 points for hitting the target representing the man who killed my Tubby, 40 for the hunters who killed the reindeer, 30 for the man who took our Kay's products, and the 20 for Nancy who killed the kittens. With this incentive, I soon become a sharpshooter. I rarely miss a target, and my addition skills also improve. On the shady side, by trial and error, I also learn the knack of operating both machines without inserting coins by tilting them. I am going to hell for sure.

Meanwhile, Kuz and her sister, who seem to have been sent to me to take the place of my sisters, include me in their conversations and activities. They take me tobogganing almost every evening, pulling me swiftly up and down Main Street. Both of them urge me to hang on as they take turns forcing the toboggan to skid around them in a circle at high speeds on the icy roads. I also study with them in the Main Street Bedroom, reminding me of the old days spent with Mattie.

Christmas Day is extremely quiet because it is too cold and stormy for my sisters to travel with the babies, and Kuz and her sister have gone home for the holiday. My favorite present is a mirror, brush, and comb set from Small Sis. A light blue wavy design on the back of the mirror and brush reminds me of the water at the lake and summer that seems so far away I can hardly bear the thought of it. Med Sis gives me a skirt holder with red clips, so I spend most of the holiday organizing my closet. Mom, Daddy, and I eat supper alone and retire early for the night.

The painful winter continues. I suffer through a severe bout of whooping cough in February; Baby Duke contracts it at the same time, but we both survive. My hatred for winter deepens like the drifts of snow outside. I associate winter with disease, which is indiscriminate, striking even an innocent infant. I harbor such questions as, why would God create such a harsh climate? why would anyone consider living in it? did Jesus know that the western continents existed? and, if not, why not? I am convinced that hell will not be a furnace—it will be a freezer.

40

At Mom's request, Daddy found her a job as a cook for a work crew on the railroad. He tried to have her hired on with his gang, but the position was already filled. All that was available was an opening way up north in the spring, but she accepted it because she is desperate to earn some money. I wonder what will happen to me when she leaves. My question is answered when she asks Small Sis and Knight if they would open up a cafe at our place. They agree to try it for a year or two and we develop a plan—Small Sis will stay in town to run the cafe; I will help her and baby-sit; and Knight will farm and ice-fish helping out with the cafe whenever he can. It is all settled.

Knight seems to relish the idea and immediately begins to renovate the store. He pulls out the shelves, leaving only a partial counter for the till. I am happy to see the boxes go because I no longer have to whack them every night before going to bed. Then one of his friends offers to help. Along the west wall, approximately three feet away from it, they build a waist-high partition with three small tables attached to it. Serving can be done over it. Their next project is to set up a counter perpendicular to the end of the partition that runs in front of the wall and between the two doorways leading into the kitchen. They cover the counter and the small tables with beige-toned arborite patterned with geometric shapes. In front of the counter they install six chrome stools with red vinyl seats that can spin around.

Behind it they hang narrow shelves on pegboard to hold cigarettes, candy, chocolate bars, and gum. The wooden floorboards are covered with gray linoleum, giving the room a clean look. The games are taken away by the vending-machine man and replaced with a soft drink cooler.

Mom sells Bossy and gives the chickens and ducks away. I can't believe what is happening. She leaves for the work gang after Easter. I don't cry and must admit that Johnny is right again, as I am getting used to saying good-bye. Small Sis quickly becomes an organized cook, cleaning up after herself as she works. I help with dishes, serving, and looking after the baby. He walks at ten months; and everyone worships him and considers him to be a genius.

I am eager to return to school after Easter break to meet the new girl who moved into town. Even though she is in the grade below mine, we hang around together. She has shoulder-length blonde hair, which she wears combed away from her long forehead, a pug nose, and white lashes framing small blue eyes. She thinks she is our town's answer to Sandra Dee so I nickname her "Dee." Our favorite pastimes are riding our bikes, reading magazines, doing homework, and winding our hair in pin curls every night as we listen to "Grey Wolf,' "The Cisco Kid," or "The Lone Ranger" on the radio.

My twelfth birthday comes and goes. In class, my attention no longer focuses on my studies. I am very much distracted by thoughts of the baby killdeer and the baby with Down Syndrome. After school, I listen to my music box play "Fascination" as I zigzag Granny's combs into my hair and daydream about how I will one day leave this end-of-the-line place. Med Sis and Small Sis are both pregnant again. I just know Big Sis won't have any more kids. I am getting taller and notice that my body is changing as I am starting to grow boobs. I still don't know which boy I am going to marry. I decide to discuss my predicament with Johnny. At the rock, I begin the conversation stating, "I don't have any boyfriends yet, and I guess it's because I still don't like boys very much."

"Believe it or not, you will hold more than one boy dear to your heart in your lifetime. Two of them will die horrible deaths, one in a car accident and the other by drowning," he predicts with such certainty that I make up a lame excuse for leaving.

School is out for the summer. This time I didn't get my name on the plaque, but am not disappointed. The smart boy a grade ahead of me now shares the honor with me. I still can't believe that my name has already appeared on it twice. The high school kids are gone for good. No more students will be staying at our place because school bus service is to begin in the fall, so I move back into the Main Street Bedroom.

Small Sis is asked to cook lunch, and often supper as well, for the guys who work at the garage. Besides supper, lunch has to be a hearty meal consisting of soup, meat, vegetables, and dessert. Sometimes, guests of the owner also join them. Eventually, the mechanic apprentice rents a room upstairs. He looks like Elvis, which is exciting to me because I am one of his biggest fans so, of course, I name him "Elvis." Imagine having Elvis living at my house! I watch him eat from a distance, day after day. He chews his food slowly and deliberately with his jaws moving under his long dark sideburns. His hair is slicked back with a giant wave in the front. He collects Elvis's records so, on almost every weeknight, Elvis's voice drifts down the stairs and into my bedroom, not that I mind. When he isn't around, Dee and I play his records and practice jiving in his room. We also spend hours in the Main Street Bedroom styling each other's hair according to instructions in movie magazines.

Backcombing and hair spraying are popular aids, and we faithfully apply the techniques to create our master-pieces. I wear a different hairdo every day. We also experiment with painting our nails different colors, including greens, blues, and sparkles. I don't tell her about the troll. He is my secret, and I am still afraid to be upstairs by myself. If, for some reason, I must go up there, I take the hammer with me and tap each step loudly to warn him that I am on my way.

41

Telephones are coming to our town! Only a few of the business have phones that the people in town use, mainly for emergencies. The workers come to eat at our cafe and my sister is very busy. I pitch in to help as much as I can, and Mom helps whenever she comes home. She works for a couple of months and then is home for at least three weeks. Occasionally, Daddy is on vacation at the same time. Our phone is in service before the summer ends. I always do the phoning for Mom, whether it is for making an appointment in the big town or for ordering something. It is just easier for me to call than it is for her.

Dee moved from the house on the other side of the tracks to one just around the corner past the egg station. We can now run over to each other's house in a couple of minutes but talk on the phone a lot instead. Another girl developed a friendship with us over the summer. She lives on a farm a couple of miles from town, so phoning her is handy. She has dark brown hair and likes Brenda Lee so I nickname her "Lee." A couple of weeks after school starts, Dee and Lee have their hair styled in the big town; cut short, I suppose, to look more like the Sandra and Brenda. Lee is in my Grade VII class and sits ahead of me.

Med Sis has another boy, "Duke II", in October; and Small Sis gives birth to a girl, Mom's first granddaughter, in November. When I look into her blue eyes for the first time, I name her "Princess Blue Eyes". Everyone says she looks quite a bit like me. All this time, I was under the impression that I inherited my dad's features but now realize I must look like my mom, too, in order for the baby to resemble me. Mom takes extra time off to help my sister run the café and adjust to caring for two babies.

Another boarder, a truck driver for the transfer business in town, moves in upstairs. He often drinks too much and is mean when intoxicated. His eyes narrow into slits, and he slurs nasty comments under his breath at everyone in his path, even though we try to avoid him when he comes home from the hotel. He is married and has a son the same age as Knight I. His family lives in the big city. He hauls freight into town from the city, spends a few days with us, and then takes a load back.

Med Sis and her family spend Christmas Day with us. With Mom and Daddy at home, too, we are all together once more. I dress Princess Blue Eyes in a pretty pink dress decorated with ribbons, lace, and frills and slip a matching bonnet over her dark hair. She looks like a doll, very much like Grandy. I wear a bluish-green corduroy dress, which I ordered from the catalogue. To make the bodice fit perfectly, I took the sides in on the sewing machine. It has a dropped waist-line with the skirt flaring out slightly at the hips. Mom allows me to order my clothes from the catalogue and place the charges on the budget plan. My favorite Christmas present is a ponytail clip from Small Sis. It is about an inch wide and features three double rows of small pearls divided by golden inserts.

The snowfall was unusually heavy all winter, and mountains of snow lined Main Street for weeks. Then spring came suddenly, causing the snow to melt too quickly. One day, while walking home from school, Dee and I meander out of our way around pools of water. She usually stops at my place, but I don't invite her in because I plan to clean my room.

Mom is home again. After chatting with her for a moment, I head for the Main Street Bedroom, which is my haven away from the kids. I stack my binder and books on Granny's writing table. As I straighten up the mess on my dresser, I happen to turn over my blue mirror. It is cracked straight down the middle from top to bottom. I just know that my nephew is responsible. He sees me inspecting the mirror and takes off for the kitchen. As I run after him, he turns and throws the toy truck he had in his hand hitting me below my right eye and making me angrier. I catch him by the arm as Mom comes around the corner. "Let him go," she hollers. "He's just small," she adds as if that makes it okay. I obey, as usual, and hurry back to my room to check the injury. A blood blister has already formed near the corner of my eyelid, which also begins to swell. If I did that to one of my mom's precious grandsons, I would be punished. The fact that boys can do no wrong and are never disciplined by their parents or grandparents leaves me enraged. No wonder they turn out to be such morons, I conclude, making myself feel better. I continue cleaning as if nothing had happened, with yet another incident involving boys left unresolved to smolder on my back burner.

Mom hires a carpenter to do some work on our living quarters. He blocks off the arched entrance to the Main

Street Bedroom and the doorway, separating the living room and old kitchen. Doors that open into a newly-created hallway are hung in the bedroom and in the living room, which becomes another bedroom. Then he installs a picture window in the living room that was the old kitchen and panels the rooms with wallboard. Mom orders a chesterfield and chair, a coffee table and end tables, and printed drapes to match the living room furniture. New linoleum is laid in every room. Mom's job appears to already be paying off, as we are more comfortable than ever before, and the place is easier to keep clean. I enjoy my newly renovated Main Street Bedroom more than I could ever have imagined.

Now I have a door with a lock that keeps out the other kids, making it possible for me to display my treasured belongings. I line up Frenchie's owl, my brush and comb sets, the jewelry box, and the trinket holder on the dresser in front of its round mirror. Then I set Granny's dictionary on the writing table within easy reach. Grandy and my other dolls, which I prop up on my bed along the wall, watch and share my every move.

My present from Mom for my thirteenth birthday arrives in the mail. It is a heavy cardigan with a cable design on the front and a ribbed collar. I also receive a letter from Daddy in which he writes that he has a pass for me to travel out east to visit my sister again in July. I perform well at my track events on Field Day, and my name is inscribed on the plaque again.

After walking home by myself on the last day of school, I decide to take a bike ride and visit the spot where I saw the end of the rainbow. Then I turn around and pedal across town to the site of the baby killdeer's grave. It is still there with the rocks undisturbed and partially covered with grass. I tug at the tall sprouts, pulling them out by the roots. After paying my respects, I head for home, push my bike into the shack, and sit on the back step. The door is open, and Hattie is visiting with Mom in the kitchen. Obviously, they aren't aware of my presence because Mom is complaining about what a tomboy I am and how I am always running, high jumping, and riding my bike. She repeats the fact that I have absolutely no interest in boys. Later that evening I recall their conversation, giving me the incentive to wear my new dress and shoes that I ordered from the catalogue. The shirt-dress is dark green with an all-over design of tiny brown flowers on stick stems. It has one large button that closes the front opening, short sleeves, and a slightly flared skirt. The shoes are dark brown with a pointed toe and a narrow two-inch heel. They have a narrow band across the top decorated with a tiny button on the side. I dig through my sisters' old bras and try them on until I find one that fits. I quickly and expertly style my hair into a French twist fastening it with only three bobby pins. Then I step into the dress, pulling its wide matching belt tightly around my waist. I practice walking in the shoes for a few minutes, take one last look in the mirror, and slip out the back door without Mom's seeing me. She is at the kitchen counter so I holler, "I'm going to the movie." As I approach the café across the street, I notice one of the guys from high school leaning against the building.

His mouth drops open as I walk by; and he blubbers as if to himself, "Wow, did you fill out over night!" I smile my sweetest smile as I think of Johnny's promise that I would, one day, be a pretty woman. I am aware of the fact that the other boys notice my transformation from the way they gawk at me. The movie is a typical cowboys and Indians feature—shoot, shoot, kill, kill and some innocent girl waiting for some cowboy to carry her off into the sunset. I find myself more absorbed in my thoughts than in the movie. I can see why Mom is so concerned with my lack of interest in boys. Her sister found a husband when she was only fourteen, and her other daughters married young. What is wrong with me? I am thirteen and still have no prospect in sight, but is that reason enough for me to panic?

42

Our town is celebrating Dominion Day with a picnic and ball tournament at the grounds behind Mom's church. My plan is to walk over and watch some ball games by myself, as usual. I decide to wear my gold, turquoise, and beige striped shorts topped with a light turquoise sleeveless blouse that buttons in the back. I pull my hair into a ponytail and hold it in place with an elastic band and my pearl clip. After entering the gate, I head straight for the ball diamond. The sun is shining brightly overhead; it's a perfect day. I stand at the side of the bleachers for a moment; I'm about to move on when my attention is drawn to the face of a young man sitting on a blanket behind the screen. His blonde curly hair is cut short with the sides brushed back. We make eye contact and his smile broadens as he nods at me—that is one boy whose smile could melt all of the icy feelings I have built up toward the opposite sex over the years. I can't help but notice that his eyes are the same color as the sky. Mine study the outline of his face with its square jaw. I know he plays in a local band because girls at school talk about him all of the time. The girl he is sitting with will be attending our school next year. She is wearing a white shirt with the collar turned up, a white pair of shorts, and white sneakers.

Her blonde hair is cut short, and the only thing missing is the white bow.

He looks so handsome in his baseball uniform that I let out an audible sigh, not caring who hears it. When his team plays, I deliberately stand in one spot for the entire game to watch him and find myself cheering out loud when he hits a ball hard and scores a home run. I'd love to play on his team—he could be my captain any time. As I walk home in the early evening, I am surrounded by his smile. I must name him "Sunny" because the sun must have had something to do with that smile—it just wasn't natural. I head for my rock intending to speak to Johnny about him. "I saw this guy today, and he is so adorable I can't stop thinking about his smile," I swoon hoping Johnny will agree with me.

"Yes, I know how you feel. You'll be happy to know that he has the personality to go with his looks," Johnny complies.

"Please, please, please, tell me more about him," I plead with Johnny.

"If I tell you more about him, I'll have to tell you more about you. I can see you at a dance in town. There is a blizzard outside, but everyone is having a good time inside the hall. You take off your brown, black, and gray plaid coat with the cowl collar and hang it with the girls' coats. As usual, the girls sit on the far side of the hall and the boys stand at the front entrance checking them out. You are wearing a pale yellow woven wool outfit. The top has long sleeves, a jewel neckline, and buttons down the back. The slim skirt is knee-length with a slit in the back. You are wearing the brown pointy-toed shoes. Your only piece of jewelry, which you wear above your heart, is a broach that has narrow golden petals flaring out from a pearl in the center. Your hair is pulled back into a French twist. You cringe as you watch the stubby guy who always asks you to dance walking toward you across the floor, but you agree to dance with him.

"Sunny is on the stage playing the fiddle in his country band. You can sense his eyes on you as you dance with your back towards him. The feeling is so intense it's as though Sunny and you are the only two people in the room. Then, as your partner turns you around, Sunny treats you to that smile and mimes a 'Hi' making your heart do a flip-flop. You lower your gaze as his eyes continue to watch you through the entire set of three dances that seems to last forever. Then I see you sitting on the bench with the other girls. You are afraid to look up because you know Sunny is there in front of you. When you do, your eyes meet as he asks you to dance. You notice that someone has taken his place in the band, which begins to play a slow waltz; "The Black Velvet Waltz" and you dance together as though you are floating on a cloud. 'You're a good dancer,' he whispers; but, before you can reply, he asks, 'May I take you home?'

"'My boyfriend is supposed to come to the dance later. He's gone to pick up a friend at the bus,' you explain, annoyed that he didn't attend the dance with you. You should know by now that he will always choose to be with the guys.

"'If he doesn't show up, please consider coming with me,' he proposes, as you continue the remainder of the dance in silence, enjoying the feel of your arms around each other. He guides you to your seat with this hand in the small of your back and returns to take his place on the stage.

"One of the girls from your class asks, Did he ask to take you home?' Another one adds, 'He broke up with his girlfriend.'

"'If I were you, I would go. Nothing would stop me,' yet another asserts with envy. You check your watch nervously wondering if your boyfriend will pick you up like he promised. He doesn't show up, and it's the end of the dance.

"Sunny walks up to you and says, 'I'm going to haul the band equipment to the car. You decide. I'll be back in a few minutes.' You have your coat on when he returns. He takes your arm urging, 'Come on.' Your mind is made up and you walk out with Sunny. You aren't prepared for the amount of snow the storm left behind and follow him as he forges a path for you through the deep drifts. His car is covered with a thick blanket of snow disturbed only on the trunk when he put in the band equipment and on the driver's door when he opened it to start the car to allow it to warm up. He opens the door and you slide in across the seat. He hasn't yet cleared off the windows. Inside, the car feels safe and warm, apart from the rest of the world—like a cocoon. He moves in close beside you and finds some soft music on the radio. 'Come here, Beautiful,' he murmurs as he draws you near. He begins to kiss your lips and you know that this is a kiss of a lifetime—one that you will never forget..."

"Johnny, stop. Don't tell me any more. I don't want to know how the kiss or the story ends." I leave the rock concerned about Sunny. I already know that he is one of the boys who will be special to me, but I don't want him to be one of the two who dies. It can't be. I won't ever let it happen.

43

I begin packing Frizzy's suitcase because Daddy and I will soon be leaving for Big Sis's. Visiting with her family would be a change for me, but I expect to keep on doing dishes, cleaning, and baby-sitting just as I have been when helping Small Sis. Daddy spends a couple of days at home, and then we are on our way. I am wearing my green dress and brown shoes. Most of my time is spent staring out the window and thinking about Sunny, his smile, and the kiss Johnny promised me. We endure a long wait in the big city. The station is exactly as I remember it from the trip I made four years ago. Then the gate is opened, and Daddy and I rush through to board our train. As I carry Frizzy's suitcase, I am startled when someone grabs part of the handle from behind me and turn around to see who it is. "Bon jour, Mademoiselle," a porter calls as he hurries along beside me taking control of the suitcase. "Into this coach," he commands in his French accent. I oblige and follow him up the steps. He chooses a seat for us and slides our suitcases onto the top rack. Then he tends to the other passengers and winks at me whenever he makes his way down the aisle. He reminds me of Frenchie so I name him "Frenchie II." He has the same accent, the same build, and the same black hair. Whenever he takes a break, he offers me pop or a chocolate bar. "One day, you must learn to speak French," he says. "All beautiful women should speak French... It suits a beautiful woman to speak French. And you should also wear Chanel No. 5. That is the perfume for you… All beautiful women should wear Chanel No. 5... Chanel No. 5 suits a beautiful woman." Time passes quickly with his joking and teasing. Nausea wells up in me after the second day of trip, but I don't become as ill as the first time. We must transfer again in the big city out east. Frenchie II helps us with our luggage but boards the train again as he continues on his way to the coast. I wave to him in the coach window as Daddy and I head for the station.

Czar picks us up at the station. My sister greets me at the back door with tears and a hug. She knows I am curious to see her youngest son, so she calls for him as I follow her to the stairs. He is the fourth son, and I am the fourth daughter—perhaps, we are both mistakes.

I can't believe that he is coming down the stairs hanging onto the handrail all by himself. Doctors were certain he wouldn't walk until he was five and would never climb stairs, yet, here he is, at only two years and three months of age, doing the impossible. He is cute even though he has predominant Down Syndrome features. His blonde hair is cut very short. My sister always dressed her boys in the latest fashions. He is wearing a striped T-shirt, tan shorts, and black oxfords with white socks. His ankles wobble as he walks toward me at the bottom of the stairwell. I stretch out my arms and say, "Come give me a hug. I'm Auntie."

He manages to come out with, "Tee," and wraps his arms around my neck. As I hold him close, I feel the elasticity of his body. A lump forms in my throat and tears well up in my eyes. I can't believe that he even fells different from my other nephews. It is an emotional meeting, to say the least, and we hit it off right then and there. He takes my hand and leads me down the hallway, through the living room and kitchen, and into the yard to his wagon.

"Take him around the block," my sister calls from the

kitchen window. "He likes to watch the trains." I help him onto the wagon, and he holds onto the sides as I pull him along. The north end of their block runs parallel to the tracks across the highway. We sit on the grassy boulevard, and he watches the trains while I study his face. I can tell he is fascinated by the different sounds—the whistling and tooting, the roar of the engines, and the banging of the cars as they hitch together. Perhaps his sense of hearing and, for that matter, all of his senses, are different from ours.

I have the north room of the second floor to myself; Daddy decides to sleep in the basement where it is cooler. He leaves for work a week later without me. I am not ready to end my visit and feel confident about traveling home alone. I spend most of my time helping my sister around the house and baby-sitting. The kitchen is small and swelteringly hot. We are often forced to take a break from doing dishes to sit outside in the shade to cool off. I help her fold heaps of laundry and iron for hours. Canning cherries and making pies proves to be a new and enjoyable experience. I attack each cherry with a stainless steel gadget; I eat almost as many as I pit.

My sister is too busy to entertain me and orders Czar I to show me around. I don't think he is too thrilled about the idea and neither am I, as our relationship is still overshadowed by the bottle cap incident. Years ago, we were pretty much the same height; but now he is much taller. He takes long strides when we walk over to see his new junior high school, and I must run every so often to keep up with him. It is a long building with an arched roof, much more impressive than my little school. He also takes me for another trek downtown and along the canal. After a day of trying to keep up with him, I come to the conclusion that people in the city do more walking than those who live in the country. After seeing us hanging around together, his friends are anxious to know about the "broad" accompanying him. He can't wait to tell them I am his aunt. Of course, they don't believe him.

After spending six weeks with my sister, we develop a deep bond. When the time comes for me to leave, she cries at the station and confesses she likes having a girl around. She could discuss things with me that she couldn't with the boys. When we talked privately, we laughed and cried as we bared our souls. I grew up around elderly people and often felt like an old person trapped in a young body. As I result, I found I could easily and comfortably communicate with people of all ages. The trip back home provides me with some much-needed time to myself. Constantly daydreaming about Sunny, I stare out the window at the monotonous scenery consisting of jagged rock walls sparsely dotted with spindly spruce trees.

44

I am already looking forward to the end of Grade VIII, but the new term is just beginning. After three years spent in the same classroom, the days have become predictable with the same teacher and same routine for too long. Only the pages of the texts are different. The hormones of the girls in my class are also changing—evidence being that everything is funny. Dee, Lee, and I giggle constantly in class, and Dee and I giggle more on the way home. The teacher is often annoyed with us, but we get away with murder because she has grown close to us over the years. Yes, we are like one big happy family.

When Daddy comes home the beginning of October, he buys a brand new television and sets it up on a shelf in the café. Now when his old friends come over, they don't play cards any more as they all sit with their eyes glued to the TV, watching everything and anything on our one and only black-and-white channel. Everyone in our district watches the same programs, so all of the conversations in town now revolve around what happened on "Bonanza," "Carol Burnett," or "The Ed Sullivan Show." After the old men start buying their own televisions, ours is moved into the living room; they continue to play cards in the café. I enjoy watching classic movies featured as matinees on the weekend or as late night shows during the week. Wicked women like Bette Davis and Barbara Stanwyck are among my favorite stars.

The new winter jacket I ordered from the catalogue arrives in the mail. It is black with four large concave golden buttons and black pile on the cowl collar and cuffs. I wear it to school the very next day. Then Dee and I walk home together, as usual. She is acting goofy and begins to yank at my jacket. I am annoyed and tell her to stop it, but she grabs my jacket by the front opening and gives it another hard jerk tearing the fabric behind the lower buttonhole. Then she has the nerve to laugh, but I don't think it is very funny. I say nothing but feel like punching her in her pug nose. "Friends like her I can do without," I mumble to myself later that evening as I do my best to mend the L-shaped tear with a needle and black thread.

Christmas comes and goes without much notice. In February, I get my period. Some consolation is the fact that I will be buying those boxes wrapped in brown paper for myself and not for my sisters. Perhaps, one day, I will get my name into the book of world records for buying feminine products for the longest "period" of time. Timing is crucial for the trip to the store; I venture out very early or later in the day when I am sure the old gossips won't be in attendance or I might be tempted to rip a box open for them. Now I am all grown up! Dee and Lee often brag about going for car rides with the older guys, and both have been kissed. As for me, I keep to myself.

When Mom comes home for Easter, Knight informs her that they are moving back to the farm because they are losing money operating the café. Besides, their kids are getting older; and they don't want to raise them in town. Mom is disappointed but understands. They plan to leave the end of April, and they invite me to stay at the farm with them. The truck driver moved out and is renting a house across the tracks with his family from the big city. Elvis and another mechanic will continue to live upstairs, and a teacher agrees to rent the Main Street Bedroom for the remainder of the school term and for the following year. Mom likes the idea of their staying at our place to keep an eye on things and to maintain the oil-burners. Daddy replaced the wood heater in the kitchen with a large oil-burner so they don't have to worry about the wood supply any more. Whenever Mom or Daddy comes home, I will stay with them.

Small Sis and I make a trip into the big town for the last load of supplies, which she purchases from a wholesaler, who loads them into the back of the truck. When we return home, we realize there is an extra box. We hastily open it to find that it is full of notebooks, the kind I use for school. Most of the time, I was scrimping for money trying to scrape enough together to buy school supplies. To me, this box of notebooks represents a gift from someone who owes me— be it Santa Claus, the Easter Bunny, or even the priest from Mom's church. I don't feel the least bit guilty about keeping it as I worked hard and never got a cent for what I did. That wholesaler overcharged us for everything anyway. We carry the box upstairs and shove it into the closet behind the bridesmaid dresses.

It is Saturday night of the last weekend of the Easter holiday. I happen to be looking out the Main Street café window when a car pulls up in front of our place. Dee and Lee are inside waving, so I run out to talk to them. The driver invites me to join them. His nickname is Buzz, and I always thought he looked a bit like Sunny. I tell Mom that I am going for a ride and hop into the car. We drive around for quite some time and then park by the grain elevator where Buzz pulls me close and gives me my first kiss. It is a long, slow, firm kiss, which makes me tingle all over. We listen to the radio, talk, and neck some more. Then we drive Lee home. When we come back into town and pass our place, I notice the front light blinking on and off. I am familiar with that signal because Mom used it on my sisters when she decided it was time for them to come in so I ask Buzz to drop me off. I float into the house with my lips still aglow from Buzz's kisses.

Mom goes away again. The weekend after she leaves, Dee invites me to her place for a sleep-over. When I arrive, she seems to be acting kind of strange and informs me that her parents are gone to visit relatives for the night. I don't think anything of it. Later in the evening, Buzz and a friend of his show up at the door. They have been drinking. Obviously, Dee invited them over without telling me. We watch a movie on TV, sit around, and talk. It is getting late so I take Dee aside and tell her we have to get rid of them. I know Hattie can see Buzz's car from her kitchen window. Being the gossip that she is, if they stay any longer, she will tell Small Sis; she'll probably tell her anyway, because she would love to see me in trouble. After trying to convince them to leave, they won't listen. Then Buzz follows Dee into her parents' bedroom. Moments later he is kissing her, and they are both giggling. I am really ticked off but decide to do nothing because they both don't deserve my attention. After Buzz's friend leaves, I move into Dee's bedroom because I can't stand listening to them so I close the door and curl up on her bed. When she comes into the bedroom, much later, I pretend to be asleep. Buzz must have spent the night on the chesterfield because I hear his car leave at daybreak. When I get home the next morning, Small Sis meets me at the door. She is upset and crying, mumbling that Hattie said she saw Buzz's car at Dee's house all night just as I predicted. I look her square in the face and say, "Buzz was drunk and fell asleep on the chesterfield. I knew Hattie would see the car and tell you. Don't worry about me. Nothing happened." I am tempted to add, "And I'm still a virgin," but I don't. Soon everybody in town is gossiping about the incident, thanks to Hattie and the old men at the store. I decide I have had enough of girlfriends and boyfriends. They are nothing but trouble. Later in the week, I am walking home from school by myself when Buzz pulls up beside me offering me a ride home. I tell him to find Dee instead. As far as I am concerned, she can have him. He parks the car and runs to catch up with me in an attempt to apologize, but I won't listen. I tell him to bug off. Finally, he gets the message and leaves. I really don't care.

45

Moving to the farm provides me with a convenient means of escape from Dee and Buzz. I have not yet forgiven them for the sleep-over incident. After carrying my belongings in from the truck, I look out the kitchen window. I estimate that the farm house is located roughly the same distance away from the teacherage road as the Main Street Bedroom is from the tracks in town. The farm road runs straight along a field and then curves between the house and the well. It continues along in front of the storage sheds toward the chicken coop with the barn on the right and makes a sharp turn west to the grain fields. All of the farm buildings are painted red, except for the house and toilet, which are white. The toilet is partially hidden in a grove of poplars and shrubs behind the house. The south edge of the yard is defined by a row of seven spruce trees.

The house appears small from the outside, but it has a large kitchen with a wood-burning cook stove. The far wall is lined with cupboards, a white enamel sink embedded in a gray arborite countertop, and a built-in white refrigerator with rounded corners. A table with chrome legs, a red arborite top, and matching chairs stands under the window, which faces the chicken coop. A wringer washer occupies the corner across from the fridge. The other window, next to the kitchen door, faces the main road. If the door is opened too wide, it strikes the wood box in the corner. Next to the wood box is the doorway to the spacious living room, whose windows, covered with venetian blinds, run along the east wall. There is a black chesterfield under the windows with a matching chair in one corner. A television in the opposite corner and another chair equipped with a telephone on a shelf in the corner by the doorway are the only other pieces of furniture. Another doorway across the room from the windows opens into a long, dark pantry and the stairwell. The two bedrooms upstairs are small with a low angled ceiling. I set Frizzy's suitcase down in the north room with the window facing the barnyard. Princess Blue Eyes and I will share the double bed. I unpack, placing some of my clothes in a small cupboard and hanging the rest in a closet under the eaves. My sister, her husband, and their son will sleep in the other room, which offers a great view of the spruce trees and clothesline. We will be crowded, but comfortable enough, and I consider myself lucky to have a place to sleep.

A one-ton truck becomes my school bus. When it stops to pick me up, someone who boarded it earlier reaches for my hand, pulls me in, and helps me to sit down. The high box is covered with a canvas tarp with no openings. It takes some time for my eyes to adjust to the darkness. Then I see the other students sitting on wooden benches lining the sides of the truck box. By that time we are already at school, because the trip lasts only a couple of minutes.

On my fourteenth birthday, the truck driver's wife and two boys happen to drop in for a visit. She is a smoker and asks for an ashtray as soon as she sits down at the kitchen table. Within minutes of her arrival, my sister and I are, also, both puffing on a cigarette. I don't particularly like the taste. However, I feel very grown up smoking with them. My sister had placed my cake in the oven just before her friend pulled into the yard. After visiting for a while, my sister adds some wood to the stove that isn't producing enough heat. She decides to empty the ashes and carries the container outside. The truck driver's wife compliments her on how clever she is to operate such a stove. We can hardly wait for her to leave so that we can share her comment with Knight, who has gone into town for the mail.

He returns with a parcel for me from Mom soon after our visitors leave. After a hysterical discussion about operating the stove, my attention focuses on the present. Inside are two skirts that my mother hand-sewed. A lump forms in my throat as I try them on. I know she cares about me but never said so in words I longed to hear. The waistbands fit perfectly. Both cotton skirts are of the same style, gathered at the waist and very flared. One is brown with a border print of peasant girls wearing red kerchiefs, black skirts, and white blouses and carrying various vases and baskets filled with flowers and fruit. The other is covered with splashes of dark blue, bright blue, orange, and white in a design that mimics wavy water shining in the sunlight. I can't wait to wear them to school. There is also a little box in the parcel, which I open to find a china ornament. It is a wicker basket with white fur lining the edge. Three kittens stand up in it with their paws resting on the fur. It is so cute and makes me think of the book Big Sis sent to me years ago. Mom also includes a note informing me that we will be visiting her again because she has applied for rail passes for the two of us. I put my presents away and then watch my sister frost the cake as soon as it cools. After supper, they sing "Happy Birthday" to me as I blow out the candles.

Med Sis announces the birth of her baby girl by phone on May 20. It is exciting to have another girl in the family. When I see her for the first time, I name her "Princess Green Eyes" and predict that she will have curly hair like the Dukes. I am now something of a hair expert, having taken on the role of family hairdresser, with my skills showing constant improvement from practicing on my sister, brother-in-law, and other members of the family. One day, Small Sis dares to volunteer for a haircut. I oblige by snipping away at it and cutting it shorter and shorter as I try to even out the length on both sides and end up tapering it in the back of her neck. She is pleased with the style until one of the neighbors takes it upon herself to console her by saying, "It will be okay in a couple of months, when it grows out."

My brother-in-law's hair is naturally wavy and nice to work with. I often shampoo and style it, taking my time as I roughly towel dry it, slop on the cream, and work my magic. One night, as I wait for him to finish his shave at the kitchen sink, I line up my styling products on the table expecting him to take a seat in my hairdressing chair. Without warning, he turns around and begins chasing me with the saving cream. Grabbing me from behind, he is about to brush the lather on my face when I grab his worn T-shirt and pull. He lets me go, but I hang on and rip it right off his body leaving only the ribbing around his neck. We stand there speechless facing each other. Then I blurt out, "Nice necklace." He can't control himself and bursts into laughter along with my sister, who watched the entire incident unfold. I join in, and we laugh until tears run down our cheeks.

Visiting the outdoor toilet with my sister before going to bed is one of my favorite rituals. She sits on the big hole and I sit on the little one just as we did years ago in town. We leave the door open to allow the moonlight to pour in. If it happens to be a lucky night, a whip-poor-will calls to us as we sit there. The bird is rare and haunts only a few farms in the area repeating its name over and over again. Sometimes, when it comes to the middle of its name, it stops as if forgetting what it has to say and starts again at the beginning. Another place for us to sit and chat is in the old sauna behind the outhouse. Its weather-beaten shingle siding renders it barely visible in the thick grove of trees. Inside the shack, there are two little rooms. The front one serves as a change room with shelves and nails on the walls for hanging up clothes and towels. The back room houses the steaming area. Fair-sized granite rocks are stacked in a circle to cover a metal stove in the middle of the room. Two benches are attached to the far wall, a lower bench and one halfway up the wall where those who like the heat can sit. Small barrels beside the heating apparatus are kept full of rainwater. Hanging next to the barrels is a dipper, used to douse the rocks in order to produce the steam once the fire in the stove heats up the rocks enough. Water in the pots on top of the stove is used for sponge bathing after perspiring. Whenever the steam hits me, I can't help but recall the bricks and vinegar incident and experience a choking sensation. Sometimes, I go for a steam bath alone after the others are done. On one of those occasions, I notice I have pubic hair. It takes me by surprise—one day it isn't there and the next day it is. Another memorable sauna moment occurs when my sister and I are sitting on the top perch late one night. She confides in me in a small voice, "I think I'm pregnant... Again. My nipples are a dark brown and my stomach looks like it. What will people think?"

"You're getting to be like Mom, always worried about what people think. Who cares? As long as the baby is okay," I reply. "Besides, you have to keep up with Med Sis," I add trying to make light of the situation and succeeding because we end up howling with laughter and can't stop. While rocking back and forth, we grab on to each other to avoid slipping off the bench, which is saturated with soapy water. According to her calculations, the baby is due on Christmas Day.

46

Duke's brother is getting married in June. My sisters ask me
if I would consider baby-sitting the five kids at Med Sis's
farm because they want to attend the wedding with their
husbands and her in-laws. Even though Princess Green Eyes
will be less than a month old, I feel confident about handling
all of them. The day of the wedding arrives, and everyone
leaves for the reception. I make supper for the kids and
clean up after them as they eat. Suddenly, Duke I blurts out,
"I have to do my job!"

"That's nice," I reply as I continue to wipe off the table.

After a few moments, he repeats the words in a more
urgent manner. "I have to do my job! I have to do my j-o-o-
o-o-b!" he howls.

"So what kind of job do you have to do?" I query as he
begins to panic. I notice his scalp turning red through the
sparse curly white hair. Deeming the situation serious, I
grant him my undivided attention. He squirms around in
discomfort for a few seconds. When he grabs his bum, I
realize what he means and rush him to his potty. I undo the
buttons on his overalls with haste, and we make it in the
nick of time. Trying to keep a straight face is difficult, but I
don't want to embarrass him. When Small Sis's kids needed
to use the potty, they used the word, "kaka," which was one
of the many cute Ukrainian words and phrases applied to
children's needs. I realize that his grandmother must have
taught him the English version of asking to go to the

bathroom and conclude, from the potty incident, that we are slowly, but surely, losing our Ukrainian heritage.

After changing Princess Green Eyes, I comfort her with a bottle, cuddle her until she falls asleep, and place her in the bassinet. I read the other three a story and separate them when it is time to go to sleep using both bedrooms. Then I secure Princess Blue Eyes on the chesterfield by placing chairs along the edge to keep her from rolling off. Black clouds are fast approaching from the southwest, and I just know we are in for a thunderstorm. Lightning strikes begin as soon as it gets dark. Many hit dangerously close as storms are always bad beside the river. The roof begins to leak in several spots so I place pails to catch the droplets of water that soon turn into significant streams.

Then the power goes out. I light a candle, which is within easy reach, and peer out the window hoping my sisters would soon be home. I watch closely as a vehicle turns into the farmyard from the main road. Lightning flashes again. I don't recognize the car so I instinctively blow out the candle and grab a couple of butcher knives from the kitchen drawer and stick them between the door casing and the wallboard. A man, whose silhouette is etched in sheets of rain, is fighting his way toward the house as the wind whips angrily at his clothes. I shove my shoulder into the door sensing he knows I am alone with the kids. He turns the knob, pushes on the door, and then swears under his breath. I can tell that he has been drinking from living next door to the hotel and its alcoholics all my life. Darkness has always been my friend, and I am grateful for it because it works to my advantage helping to keep me hidden from him. My only fear is that one of the kids will wake up and begin to cry. A sudden cloudburst catches the man off guard as he stumbles away from the door. I let out a sigh of relief as I watch him stagger to the car that jerks into motion and makes its way out of the yard.

Unable to sleep, I watch the storm until its anger dissipates and the sky clears. When the sun is beginning to rise, my sisters return and I run to beat them to the door in order to remove and hide the knives. They chat for a few minutes discussing the wedding. I decide not to tell them what happened because I don't want to spoil their fun. Small Sis bundles up her kids and leaves with Knight. They aren't coming back to the celebration to be held there later that day. I stay behind.

People begin arriving for the outdoor party in the afternoon. They set up tables and chairs under the trees. It is a perfect day, clear and sunny, with no hint of the ragged clouds of the previous night. Women bring potluck to supplement the leftovers from the wedding supper. Many of the neighbors also bring their kids. Some of the visitors are elderly friends of Duke's parents. Everyone is having a good time as they help themselves to food set out on tables outside and play cards inside. After supper, some of the men are standing by the road having a smoke when one of them notices a strange object in the western sky. An old man brings out binoculars, and they take turns scanning the horizon but can't spot anything. It is getting late, and the party begins to break up. Those with small kids leave. Others make their way into the house to drink and play more cards. Just as I am about to enter the house, an old man calls to me because he sees something with the binoculars. My sister tells me to go ahead and have a look as she disappears into the porch. I approach him with caution. When I look through the binoculars, I see nothing. Then the gnarled hands are on my breasts. It's "déjà vu"; I should have known this was going to happen and been more prepared. After all, Johnny had predicted it had warned me. I'm angry with myself for allowing the prophecy to become a reality; but then, again, I might have no control over it. I force my elbows down hard and fast, knocking his hands away and causing the binoculars to drop to the ground, in what appears to be slow motion. I run to the house trembling. I feel as though I am taking part in a dream—no, a nightmare. My mind is bombarded with all sorts of questions which include, is he the same man who came to the house during the storm? did this happen to me to protect me from him in the future? and, will all of Johnny's prophecies come true?

47

I am now done with elementary school. My name was engraved on the plaque again, which is a favorable way for me to leave the classroom where I spent the last four years. My gift from Mom for passing Grade VIII is a portable stereo record player with a dark gray exterior and light gray lid. Elvis gives me some 45's that he no longer wants. He would usually subject them to the heat in the box stove and watch them slowly melt and become deformed before tossing them into the fire anyway.

I am looking forward to high school but am more excited about my summer holiday. First of all, I will make a trip by truck with my sister and her family to visit Knight's parents out east. Then I will travel by train with Mom to visit Big Sis, after which I will be back on the train for another trip up north with Mom to help her when she returns to cook for her crew.

The morning after I get out of school, my vacation begins with my helping Knight load up the truck. He has built a wooden canopy on its box, installed benches along the sides, and placed a double-sized mattress in the middle. I pack some of the kids' belongings with mine in Frizzy's suitcase and slide it under the bench with the other luggage. The kids are excited about the adventure and sit with me in the back of the truck for the first part of the trip. It isn't very pleasant, because dust from the gravel road sifts in through the floorboards and along the edges of the canopy. Eventually, we are covered from head to toe with white sediment. All we can see of each other's faces are eyes and, of course, teeth when we smile. Riding in the back becomes more bearable once we hit the paved roads and dust ourselves off.

The kids are asleep when we reach Knight's aunt's place, which is the halfway point of our journey, and where we will spend the night. They are elderly people who visit with Knight until midnight, enjoying the opportunity to speak with someone in Finnish. I take a long, hot shower to get rid of the dust. Even though I sleep with the kids, I wake up refreshed. My sister doesn't want her in-laws to know that she is pregnant again so she asks me to help her with her corset. She holds her breath while I tug and struggle to get all the hooks done up. Then she pulls on a short-sleeved cotton dress. It has alternating rows of orange and red flowers running the length of the dress from the boat-shaped neckline to the hem that falls to just below her knees. As I zip up the back of her dress, I think about how young she looks, and is,—too young to have two kids and another one on the way. The old people are up early making us breakfast. I am famished but quickly lose my appetite when I am faced with the runny undercooked eggs. Bright orange yolks stare up at me like bloodshot eyes. I know my sister is thinking the same thing because she gives me a funny look, and we force ourselves to keep from giggling. It would be too bad for her if she happens to be suffering from morning sickness. I dip my toast into the egg, chew it as little as possible, and swallow. At least the food fills me up, and I feel okay as long as I don't think about the eggs. I sweep out the back of the truck while Knight pounds the dust out of the mattress, and we continue on our way.

Knight's parents come out to greet us when we pull into their yard. His mom gives us each a hug. She is a short woman with wavy blonde shoulder-length hair, which she pins back behind her ears. I admire her lovely smile. His dad is a portly man of average height. His thinning gray hair is combed away from his forehead. He wears dark-rimmed glasses, and his left eyelid remains closed from an injury he had suffered as a young man. He speaks in Finnish to his son as we walk into the house together. She bustles about trying to make us comfortable and offers us drinks and food. Later in the evening, relatives come to visit.

We enjoy some sightseeing over the next few days and visit their famous falls. They aren't as grand as the Czars' falls but have their own special feature. Massive rocks jut out from the base of the falls to the top. When the flowing water strikes them, each one forms its own waterfall. After walking around the park surrounding the falls, we drive to the home of Knight's aunt and her husband. They live in a log cabin on the shore of a large lake. In the distance, I can just barely discern the outlines of ships moving through the thick haze. The water is cold and choppy, but I swim anyway, floating on my back and watching the puffy clouds moving along at a swift pace. I spend most of the afternoon building sandcastles on the beach with the kids. Then we stroll back to the house holding hands and enjoying the scenery. Knight's aunt introduces me to her sixteen-year-old son who walks in the door after us. He has black hair styled in a short crewcut, dark eyes, and front teeth that buck out when he smiles. I nickname him "Bucks." He was apparently waiting for our visit with the hope of returning to the farm with us. His parents think it might be a good idea because his behavior hasn't been the best of late, and Knight agrees to take him.

Within a couple of days, we are on our way home. With Bucks in the back of the truck, it's very crowded , and it is difficult for me to avoid him. I am grateful that Knight drives all night stopping only for a quick nap. The return trip is not only faster, it is also more pleasant, because we hit the dusty road at the end of the trip instead of the beginning.

I spend a couple of days at the farm and am anxious for Mom to get home because Bucks gets too close as he deliberately hangs around me and makes me feel uncomfortable. When I move into town with Mom, he shows up for a visit. In order to get rid of him, I introduce him to Dee. She can have him, too. My plan works because he starts following her around, and she likes it.

48

Mom and I leave for Big Sis's in the middle of July. I am enjoying the trip until several guys in navy uniform board the train. One of them saunters over and sits across from us trying to impress me. He is loud and boisterous. Mom is annoyed, and I wish he would leave me alone. I am tempted to punch him in his narrow face. His dark eyes are too closely set and his eyebrows, which match his black brushcut, are too thick. Whenever he leaves to join his buddies to eat in the diner, Mom and I use the opportunity to stretch our legs or retrieve items from our suitcases. I feel like I am walking on eggshells because I never know when he is going to pop up. On a couple of occasions, when I use the washroom, he doubles back to catch me because he is right behind me when I come out, rubs up against me, and even goes so far as to put his hands on me. I don't dare push him away. He is mean, and I am afraid he might cause trouble for Mom and me. After copying my name and address from the luggage tag on Frizzy's suitcase, he promises to write to me and even threatens to come and visit me one day. I hope he is joking. I am relieved when we disembark without incident in the big city and he continues on to his coastal destination.

Czar IV is happy to see me. I wonder whether he really remembers me or knows who I am because his mom told him I was coming for a visit. In any case, he calls out, "Tee, Tee," wanting me to take him for a ride on the wagon to watch the trains. He also inherited a tricycle from his brothers, and I spend hours pushing him around the block. My sister's spirit seems broken, and the sparkle in her eyes is gone. She has mastered the art of patience in caring for her son; from what I can see, she is now resigned to doing the best she can for him.

The weather is hotter and more humid than usual. Mom and I are sharing the double bed upstairs because the boys have the other room. Late one night, after I lie there for hours unable to sleep, Mom sits up with a start. "I've got a nosebleed," she whispers. I can't believe the amount of blood I see when I turn on the light. I scramble to find tissues and soak up as much of it as I can with a dark towel.

We take turns applying pressure halfway up her nostrils because she dozes off now and again. It is a long night, and I am more than relieved when the bleeding stops at dawn. I am also concerned about her varicose veins. Her legs have always been bad but have grown worse since she started working from being on her feet too much and from the heavy lifting. The heat wave is not helping her high blood pressure either. Later that morning, one of the veins in her leg bursts. As she applies pressure to stop the profuse bleeding, my sister phones her doctor. He wants to see her immediately so my brother-in-law takes her to the hospital where she has her nostril and vein cauterized. After resting for a few days, she is feeling better.

I do manage to have some fun on my vacation. I double date with one of the boys from down the street. He is a redhead with freckles sprinkled across his nose. We drive to the amusement park on the beach, try out some rides including the roller coaster, and eat candyfloss. Before leaving, we boat through the Tunnel of Love. The other couple makes noises while they kiss trying to make us laugh. My date is nice but could never measure up to Sunny in my eyes.

One of my sister's friends offers me an outfit that is too tight for her guessing it would be about my size. It looks expensive and sports a designer tag. I can't wait to try it on and am pleasantly surprised with the perfect fit. The black linen dress features a white satin collar and large bow that are worn outside the fitted bolero, which has three-quarter length sleeves. The knee-length skirt is tight with a slit in the back. Bringing my white high heels along was a good idea because they complete the outfit. I am wearing it when Mom and I say goodbye to my sister and her family. She can't control her tears and is still crying when we drive off with her husband in the direction of the station.

Mom and I are rushing along the platform to catch our train in the big city when a familiar voice from behind me calls, "Bon jour, Mademoiselle." I turn around and there is Frenchie II smiling at me. He grabs Frizzy's suitcase, ushers us onto the train, and makes sure we are comfortable before he helps the other passengers. Deciding to save the dress and jacket for special occasions, I change from the linen outfit into a white blouse and my blue skirt with the wavy design. Frenchie II and I have more time to visit than on the previous trip. He tells me about France and the tiny village where he spent his childhood, filling my head with a desire to travel and experience some of the wonders of Europe. The train gobbles up the miles without my succumbing to motion sickness. Before we know it, the time arrives for us to transfer trains in the big city. Frenchie II spends the last few minutes with me. He says, "Always remember what I told you about being a beautiful woman. Now close your eyes and open your hand." Then he places something in my palm and presses my fingers over it. As he waves from the steps of the train, he calls, "Au revoir, Mademoiselle." In the station, I slowly open my hand; and there, before my very eyes, lies a tiny bottle of Chanel No. 5. I unscrew the top carefully, take a gentle sniff, dab some on the inside of my wrist, and take a deeper sniff. Surprisingly, it does make me feel beautiful.

49

As soon as we get home, Mom tells me to run over to the post office for the mail. Our box is full. I am shocked to find three letters for me with "HMCS" stamped on the envelopes and know, at a glance, that they are from that creepy sailor. I don't even want to open them but decide to in case he is thinking of visiting me. The words he writes are as creepy as he is, and he does threaten to make a trip in our direction in the near future. I doubt that he will because we are too far off the main line.

Mom and I are home only long enough to do laundry and pack our suitcases, and Knight is driving us to the station again. The train, with its old-fashioned engine, is much slower than the express that runs from coast to coast. It does plenty of backing up, seeming to move forward five miles and then reversing six. Approximately half way to our destination, the train stops and pulls onto a siding. The conductor informs us that we will have a four-hour delay, which, apparently, is not uncommon on the route. The village nearby bears a complicated Indian name and consists of a grocery store, post office, and a few shops and houses. Mom and I decide to walk to the café. I order coffee for her and pop for myself. Then we sit on a bench outside to enjoy some fresh air. Suddenly, a car pulls up. The kids inside are about my age and strike up a conversation with me asking where I am from and where I am going. When they find out about the delay, they ask my mom if I would be allowed to go for a ride with them. I don't really want to, but they promise her they will have me back in a couple of hours. She gives me permission to go because there is such a long wait. I hesitate as I climb into the car and look back at Mom, who waves as we drive away.

After traveling for a few minutes, the driver pulls off the graveled highway and onto a dirt road running through dense bush. The car bounces over roots and fallen trees. Soft muddy spots are covered with saplings to make the road passable. We drive for some distance and come upon a clearing where they say their families often camp in tents. One of the guys opens the trunk, pulls out a case of beer, and proceeds to snap off the caps. I refuse to drink insisting I want to finish the pop that I purchased at the café. The two couples wander off into the thick brush with their beer. I sit and talk to the driver in the shade of the tall pine trees that encircle the area. Time is passing too quickly, and I begin to fear that he might not drive me back in time to catch my train. Uneasiness wells up in my stomach as I imagine what might happen to me in this secluded spot. They could beat me up and leave me here or even kill me. Nobody would ever find me it they tossed my body into the dense brush. Finally, the two couples come back, hop into the back seat, and begin necking as we speed off. The driver pulls me close and kisses me several times while he is driving. I don't dare push him away fearing that he could slip off the narrow trail and get stuck. As we turn the corner nearing the tracks, I am relieved to see the train still resting in the same position. Mom is standing outside our coach, and I can tell from the expression on her face that she is relieved to see me, too. I jump out of the car almost before it stops, and we immediately board the train. Within minutes, it jolts forward.

We arrive at the crew's work site the next afternoon. The living quarters consist of several railway cars parked on a long siding further up an embankment. The kitchen takes up one long car. The far end of the car is occupied by an enormous oil-burning cook stove and water tanks on one side with cupboards separated by two huge stainless steel sinks on legs on the other. It can be entered from both sides through doors in the middle, which divide the cooking area from the dining area that harbors a long table with benches on either side. The cook car is connected to the food storage car with a short hallway. The shelves on one side of the car are lined with rows upon rows of canned goods. On the other side stands a set of fridges and a large freezer. A corridor leads to our sleeping quarters. I admire the bunk beds as I set Frizzy's suitcase on the floor and throw my purse on the top bunk. The room is furnished with a small table, two chairs, a closet, a chest of drawers, and a washstand with a basin and large pitcher. I look out the window and notice the toilet, which is a short distance from the cars just down the hill.

Mom and I wash our faces, change into work clothes, return to the cook car, and immediately begin to peel potatoes. As she slides a gigantic roast into the oven, the bull cook comes by with a supply of water. He is young, about my height, and has dark red hair and freckles. After emptying the water into the tall containers, he helps me set the table. The smell of roast beef fills the car by the time the men file in to eat. The foreman is a stocky man with gray hair. As I help Mom serve the food, I listen to his stories and jokes. He seems to think it is his responsibility to keep the men happy. They also enjoy my company and are very polite. I quickly clear off the table when they leave. Then Mom and I sit down and eat our supper faced with stacks of dishes to wash and heavy pots to scrub. It is dark outside by the time we finish cleaning up. Most of the dishes dry quickly on racks after being rinsed with hot water. The bull cook returns to help me set the table for breakfast turning the plates upside down as he goes along, and I do the same— to keep dust and flies off the eating surface, I assume. I decide to nickname him "Bully."

Our sleeping car is sweltering hot from the heat of the oven. The long narrow window over my bunk is screened to keep out the sand and black flies that hover everywhere in swarms. I toss and turn until about midnight when a welcomed breeze blows in over my top sheet. My stomach is still full. We never ate beef at home or on the farm so I had stuffed myself. My eating a tin of crabapples for dessert didn't help either.

I work hard to give Mom a bit of a break as I am still concerned about her legs. If one of her veins ever ruptured in this isolated place, I couldn't even begin to imagine what might happen. On the whole, her health seems to be better than it was in previous years. Bully and I often walk along the tracks or into the bushes to try to escape the pesky insects, which bite mercilessly at any exposed flesh. Most of the time, we wear screened hats. We have plenty of time for long conversations. He is engaged to his high school sweetheart. We are becoming friends, but I keep my distance, not wanting the relationship to go any further.

Mom and I discover a huge blueberry patch in a narrow field running along the tracks. The fruit grows on tiny shrubs close to the sandy soil making them difficult to pick. However, we return to the cook car with our containers full. After feasting on some with cream, we still have plenty left for pies. The men enjoy the pies so much that they pick berries with us after work. Mom and I bake every blueberry dessert imaginable to the delight of the workers.

One night, after fussing with her hair in front of the mirror, Mom heads down the corridor to the kitchen. She returns with a gigantic pair of scissors resembling meat shears. "Cut my hair," she pleads. "I can't stand it any more." Like a professional stylist, I shampoo her hair, cut it, and roll it up in curlers. Then I pull a hair-dryer out of my suitcase. It has a cap with a hose attached to the heating and blowing mechanism. I plug it in and begin to pack Frizzy's suitcase for my trip home. When I turn around to check Mom's hair, I panic when I see smoke billowing out of the holes in the plastic cap. I pull the plug from the socket and rip the cap off her head. Frantically, I examine her hair and scalp.

"Nothing's burnt," I blurt out with relief. We both begin to laugh at the same time and continue until tears roll down our cheeks. In the morning, she tells the foreman about what had happened. He chuckles as he explains how the voltage of the electrical system in the cars is too high for regular appliances.

My ten days with Mom pass all too quickly. Most of the time I did the dishes myself, but Mom helps me the night before I leave. As we chat, she suggests that I stay in town with her sister instead of at the farm, at least, until Christmas. "Aunt B," as I called her, raised sixteen children, all of whom had left home. Years ago, some of them stayed at our place to attend high school. My aunt was lonely and didn't want to face an entire winter by herself. Apparently, they discussed the arrangement when Mom was home last. I agree to think about it. The foreman happens to be leaving his crew the next morning for a two-week vacation. Since we will be traveling together, he assures Mom that he will keep an eye on me.

Early the next morning, Bully comes to see me off just as the train appears. The foreman radioed the engineer ordering him to stop for passengers. Bully seems upset about my leaving, but I wish him luck on his wedding day and give him a big smile as he waves good-bye. The train is crammed with Indians. The foreman and I occupy the last empty seat at the back of the coach near a potbellied stove used for heating the car in cold weather. The air is filled with the nauseating odor of stale liquor and campfire smoke. Time passes slowly, and I can't get used to the stench. The foreman shares my discomfort and forces open a couple of windows. Whenever he goes to the dining coach, he comes back with pop, sandwiches, or other treats for me. When we arrive at the village where I was taken for the joyride, I slump down in my seat while the train is stopped afraid that someone might spot me. I slouch down farther when I see the familiar car pull up. At that very moment, the train begins to move and I breathe a sigh of relief. The kids have probably been checking every train in search of me because they know I will eventually have to board one of them on my way home.

Med Sis picks me up at the station. The foreman visits with us for a few minutes and then continues on his way to the big city. I spend a week with my sister and baby-sit most of the time while she weeds her garden and helps with the haying. Then I give Small Sis a hand with her kids for a few days before school starts. I inform them that I have decided to stay with Aunt B at Mom's request. Times were tough on the farm, and they were having enough trouble making ends meet without having to provide for me all of the time. Besides, I often felt like an intruder. So there I was packing Frizzy's suitcase again. I promise my sister that I will visit on weekends. She is beginning to show—her secret is out!

50

I think about Aunt B as Knight drives me into town. She is a small woman, her stature diminished by the chronic hunching of her back. Her gray hair is wavy along the top and sides and pulled back into a bun at the nape of her neck. She is so old-fashioned compared to my mother and always covers her head with a kerchief whenever she goes out. Her wardrobe consists of long dresses, brown stockings, and a cardigan. She always speaks to me in Ukrainian and I answer in English. Her house, a square building with red asphalt shingle siding and a green roof, is located on the edge of town beyond the tracks. My brother-in-law drops me off at the front. I grab my suitcase from the back of the truck, which pulls away leaving me standing there filled with uncertainty. I have no where else to go, so I walk around the house to the back yard where I am met by my aunt. We enter the house together. I notice that the kitchen door is directly in line with the front door, a sure sign of bad luck, according to Granny. Her home is simply furnished. A refrigerator and a wood-burning cook stove, which is flanked on one side by a small table and cupboards and a washstand on the other, fill the kitchen. It is separated from the living room with a curtain. The living room also serves as a dining area with a blue arborite and chrome table and chair set. The walls are lined with various cabinets in which she stores her belongings. A chesterfield, chair, and coffee table are the only remaining pieces of furniture on the main floor of her home.

Speaking Ukrainian, my aunt invites me to take my

suitcase upstairs. The stairs are really a rustic ladder, built of barkless spindly logs. I am reminded of climbing into the loft of the barn as I teeter on the knotted rungs, lugging Frizzy's suitcase behind me. The floor is constructed of planks that creak and bend under my weight. The bed near the stairs is hers. I make my way past the curtain dividing the room. Of the two beds in that area, I choose the one on the south side as I have learned from experience it will be the warmer of the two when the winter winds begin to blow. I unpack most of my things, set up my alarm clock, and plug in my radio. I leave my glass trinket saver, my jewelry box, and Granny's flowered storage box along with the blue owl in Frizzy's suitcase and push it under the bed. My supper has been kept warm on an enamel plate with a matching lid on the stove. As usual, I am famished; I gobble up every morsel of food that my aunt sets in front of me. Then she brings me an extra large piece of pie. As I cut off a triangle with my fork, dark raisins slither out of the sides to the outer frill of crust. I open my mouth and slide the dessert off the fork. The large raisins are so bitter that I swallow them without chewing. I don't want her to know I am struggling to finish the pie, which is difficult, because, instead of joining me for supper, she sits right in front of me watching my every move. It takes a while but I finish, smile, and compliment her on the food, the pie included. Then she won't even allow me to help her with the dishes. I just cannot believe it. I feel weird watching her as she cleans up after me, an honor never before bestowed on me. My only chores are to carry in wood and water. After filling the wood box, I take a pail and head for the well that is located just down the lane behind her neighbor's house. It looks very much like a wishing well, with a rope wound around a pulley and the end attached to a pail dangling from an arch attached to the well's sides. I unravel the rope, estimating how much I will need to reach the water and drop the pail just right, so that it tilts and takes in water. Once the pail is full, I pull on the rope that lifts the pail to the surface and then empty the water into Aunt B's bucket. Judging how to drop the pail requires skills similar to tossing beanbags or shooting rubber rings. It is a challenge, and I have plenty of time to practice as the days pass ever so slowly.

My aunt's house is a short distance from school. In fact, any point from the outskirts of town to the school is less than a ten-minute walk. On the first day of classes, I wear my wavy skirt and a white blouse. I arrange my hair in my favorite style by backcombing the front and pinning it up and letting the rest hang down my back. I am excited about being in high school but, at the same time, afraid of the change, having grown too comfortable in my old room with the same teacher for too long. I heard that the four high school teachers are all men, which makes me nervous.

I enter the building through the north door with the other high school students. Our room is small. I take a seat near the front and anxiously await the arrival of the teacher after the bell rings. There are approximately thirty of us with our desks jammed closely together. Every once in a while, someone makes a goofy comment and we all snicker, but we wouldn't be snickering for long. We all sit at attention when we hear the sharp click of heels coming down the hallway approaching our room. I know that the man who enters is the principal; he has already been dubbed "Eagle Beak" because of his large hooked nose. He is a small man wearing a gray suit, white shirt, and striped tie. His reddish-orange hair is parted on the side and combed back in a half dozen tiny waves. He has small eyes—green, I would guess— and horn-rimmed glasses that enhance the size of his nose. His lips are thin and barely move as he introduces himself. He speaks in a manner that suggests we must toe the line or suffer the consequences. History is our first subject. He quizzes us, trying to figure out how much we know and how much we must learn. I raise my hand every time and answer most of the questions so he asks my name. I introduce myself and, from that moment on, I know we will get along fine.

Eagle Beak is a no nonsense teacher with rules—no chewing gum; no holding hands with your boyfriend; if you break or lose lab or sports equipment, you are responsible for paying for it or replacing it; and, the weirdest rule of all, no opening the top of your hinged desk to get something out once he enters the classroom. In order to comply with the last one, I usually keep most of my books and belongings on the floor, creating a mess around my feet. He often comments on how he would hate to see my house, once I got married, if I kept it in the same state as the area surrounding my desk. In addition to teaching English, he also teaches us French, which proves to be interesting since he speaks with a pronounced Ukrainian accent. His teaching methods are very effective, and I learn a lot from him.

Our Math instructor is a Chinese fellow, who has the habit of scratching himself all over his torso and arms as he speaks. After a few moments in his class, many of the students are scratching themselves, too. Obviously, being itchy is catchy. I nickname him "Let 'x' be the unknown number." One of the two other teachers is fired before Christmas. I don't know why, but I never liked him anyway. Out of the blue, on many occasions, he would order us, one by one, to stand up in front of the class to give an impromptu speech, ridicule us, and order us to sit down after uttering only a few words. As a result, public speaking became my greatest phobia—I would rather strip than speak.

In the evenings, after I finish my homework, I listen to

my aunt tell stories about her family. She is so proud of her sixteen children, but often has difficulty remembering their names. Within weeks, I can identify her sons and daughters from studying the hordes of pictures that she displays on the living room table. She tells me about what they did when they were young, about where they live, and about their spouses and children. I don't have time to miss television. Besides, I lived without one for most of my life. I am most happy to be staying in town because I can run over to Granny's as often as I wish. She is almost blind but still interested in the on-going sagas of Rex Morgan and Mary Worth. Now it is my turn to read her the comics. She never wants me to leave and always begs me to stay longer as she holds onto my hand.

I wear the green shirt-dress to my first school dance. It is a special occasion and warrants dabbing some of Frenchie II's Chanel No. 5 behind my ears and on the inside of my wrists before I leave for the hall. My first dance is with a boy I saw before at the weddings I attended with my mother. His pale complexion is the symptom of a serious health problem. I know that one of the girls in my class has a crush on him. He is a wonderful dancer but very quiet. Sunny's band happens to be playing. Every time I dance by the stage, he flashes his smile at me; and I think to myself, "I'm going to kiss that boy one day."

Remembrance Day is coming, and there is an air of excitement in my aunt's house. Her youngest son and two youngest daughters are coming home from the big city, and I am invited to spend the weekend with them. She rushes around cleaning, cooking, and preparing for their arrival. Before we know it, they are at the door. Both girls look like their mom, and all three speak with the same voice. Her son has dropped his wife off at her parents' home near the city because their first baby is due soon. He is tall with wavy dark hair and a nice build. Before we eat supper, he takes off his shirt when he washes at the basin in the kitchen revealing his muscular arms and chest. Later that evening, he gives me one of his jackets to keep. It has been hanging on the hook by the ladder, and I must admit that I often admired it. It is a black velvet windbreaker with a front zipper. I graciously accept the gift and repeatedly tell him how much I love it. I can't wait to wear it to school with my jeans. We talk until the wee hours of the morning. The girls sleep in the bed across from mine, and he sleeps on the chesterfield downstairs. Their time with us passes all too quickly. My aunt cries after they leave, and there is little I can do to comfort her.

51

Filled with my belongings, Frizzy's suitcase sits in the middle of the bed. This will be my last night at Aunt B's. Mom and Daddy are coming home for an extra long holiday. After Christmas, I'll be shipped back to the farm because my sister will need my help after the new baby arrives.

There is plenty of room in the suitcase for the velvet jacket, but I am having second thoughts about keeping it. I reach for it and slip it off the bedpost as I caress the luxurious fabric with my fingertips. Without another thought, I scurry down the ladder and place the jacket back on its hook where it belongs. I realize, with surprise, that my fear of climbing down the ladder is gone. I hurry back up, snap the suitcase shut, and shove it under the bed. There are no streetlights on the outskirts of town so I always climb into bed before I pull on the string to turn out the bulb on the ceiling. As I stare into complete darkness, I think about the Main Street Bedroom and the light filtering through the curtains from the street lamp on the corner. I am longing to sleep in my bed again. I miss the nightly show of various patterns of light moving slowly along the walls as cars make U-turns between our place and the hotel. I am also looking forward to visiting with my parents. The words, which stick in my mind, seem odd so I whisper them to myself, "I am looking forward to visiting with my parents." One visits friends or relatives, but is visiting one's parents normal? I don't want to admit it; but the days, weeks, months, and years of being separated from them is chipping away at whatever bond I had with them. My sisters have become my parents. With regret, I can't even pinpoint when that critical change in my life occurred. Perhaps, my fate in this world is to be alone.

Early in the morning of December 22nd, Knight drops my little niece and nephew off in town on his way to the hospital. My sister is in labor and they aren't taking any chances. She gives birth to another son minutes after Knight and Small Sis arrive at the hospital. The day before Christmas, we wait anxiously for her to come home. Knight leaves early hoping to return within a couple of hours. Later in the afternoon, there is still no sight of them. Dee calls inviting me over to her place, and Mom tells me to go ahead. Apparently, they arrived minutes after I walked out of the house. According to Mom, my sister was pretty disappointed that I was not at home to greet the new baby and I feel guilty about not being there for her.

On Christmas morning, Mom stuffs one of Med Sis's turkeys and slides it into the oven; my sisters and their families will be coming over for supper. Daddy has a present for me. It's a pair of mukluks that he bought up north. They are made out of deerskin, with beaded embroidery hand-stitched in designs of flowers on the vamp and on the band at the top, which is also decorated with white fur. Matching pompoms adorn the ends of the leather laces that are used to tie the tops tight to keep them up and the snow out. Knight comes to pick me up and take me to the farm because the kids want me there when they open presents, so I wear the mukluks and am surprised at how warm and cozy they are, perfect for our weather.

Still in their pajamas, the kids meet me at the door. They admire my mukluks for a moment and then focus their attention on their own presents. Their dad hands them out; this reminds me of the night when I discovered there was no Santa Claus. He has a present for me, too. I carefully remove the shiny paper, to find a plush white dog with black spots, floppy ears, and a stubby tail. It's a pajama bag with a storage area in its stomach, finished with a zipper for easy access. I like it but it looks too expensive so I scold my sister, telling her that she should have used the money for a roast or something. She laughs defending the decision to buy me the dog, which is their way of saying thanks for all the help I was to her and for all the baby-sitting I have done. I apologize for not being at home when she returned from the hospital. Crying from the crib next to the Christmas tree interrupts our conversation. She picks up the baby, changes him, and hands him to me. I hold him for a while enjoying the baby warmth as I cuddle him, feed him his bottle, burp him, and place him back in his crib after he falls asleep in my arms. The kids are already bored with their toys and gather around to see what I am doing. I salvage several spruce branches from the bottom of the wood box and secure them together with brown twine. "I'm making a small tree for Granny," I explain. They help me decorate it with red crepe paper decorations. I cut a star out of cardboard and cover it with silver cigarette paper. The tree fits perfectly in the box my dog came in, and I rewrap it with the shiny paper.

After a quick snack, we prepare for the trip into town. My sister bundles up the baby while I dress the two older kids, who insist on taking their Christmas toys with them. Fortunately, Knight is driving his dad's car; their family has grown too large for the truck cab. It is a sunny day, but clouds are approaching from the north. Duke's car is already parked in front of our place when we arrive. As soon as we enter the front door, everyone crowds around to admire the baby. The kids always have a great time whenever the two families get together at our place. They twirl around on the stools and run back and forth behind the counter, up and down the hallway, and through the doorways at both ends of the kitchen.

By the time we finish eating, it has begun to snow. My sisters sort out what belongs to each kid and leave while the roads are still in good condition. Even though tranquility fills the air, the place resembles a war zone. I can't understand how things get so out of hand, compelling me to snap a photo of the counter where the kids ate. It is cluttered with dishes and littered with leftover food—a mess only they were capable of making. I tidy up a bit and stack the dishes, deciding to wash them later. I prepare a platter of food to take to Granny and Gramps along with the Christmas tree. They had turned down our invitation to join us for supper accepting the fact that they are too old to venture out in the middle of winter.

Gramps greets me at the door. Granny is sitting by the kitchen table in her rocking chair with a blanket over her knees. I help her open the present and can tell by her smile that she is delighted with the makeshift tree. As she runs her fingers over the branches, decorations, and the star, she whispers, "The smell of the spruce brings back so many Christmas memories." They eat most of the food, which is still warm, and save some for breakfast. However, I am concerned about Granny. Her health seems to be deteriorating rapidly, but I am somewhat comforted by the fact that she did eat. The wind is picking up so I don't stay long anticipating a blizzard.

I was right—the stormy weather continued for days. For most of the holiday, we remained snowbound. By Ukrainian Christmas, the wind and snowy conditions subside so I take some cabbage rolls and perogies over to Granny and Gramps. Granny doesn't get up to eat. She is lying on the couch and beckons for me to come closer. Then she takes my hand in hers and begins reminiscing about the wonderful times we had together. I listen to her in silence as I did when I was a little girl, not answering this time because I am too choked up to speak. "I know my time is near. Don't cry for me. I'll be where I want to be," she whispers. I sit with her until she falls asleep and give her a lingering hug. Gramps shows me out patting my shoulder and assuring me that everything will be okay. Glancing back, I give him a wave, just a little wave, as I hurry down the snow-beaten path.

52

By the time the temperatures plunge, I am back at the farm.
Some mornings, I awaken to find my pillow and hair frozen
to the wall. If nobody braves the cold in the night to throw
some wood in the stove our drinking water turns to solid ice
in the pail on the kitchen counter. Knight spends days, often
weeks, at the fish camp. I learn how to pack nets—untangle
the mesh and spread it in the middle of the crate while
placing corks at one end and leads at the other. We spend
entire evenings at the mesmerizing task, surprisingly, with
never a lull in our conversation.

Early one February morning, the phone rings. When my
sister hangs up, she looks at me and whispers, "Granny's
gone." Somehow, I manage to live through the next few
days. I ask for permission to leave class to attend her funeral
at the United Church. I run all the way and make it in time
for the viewing. After standing at the back of the church for
a few minutes, I move toward the front with my legs barely
supporting my body. As I pass Gramps sitting in the front
pew, he reaches out and clutches my hand. I close my eyes
for a moment before looking into the coffin. My first glance
is drawn to Granny's trifocals, which are tucked into the
breast pocket of her black dress with the buttons down the
front. Then my eyes focus on her face aglow from the
reflection of her silver hair enhanced by the shining folds of
the white satin lining of the coffin. I hear her last words,
"Don't cry for me. I'll be where I want to be," but I do cry—
large, silent tears, which fall onto my black jacket. I reach
out and touch her hand. It's cold, so cold—strange, not like I

remember it to be. The moment has come for me to let her go. I back away from the coffin, turn, and hurry to the back pew where I sit by myself. After the service I meet Gramps outside, where he introduces me to Granny's niece. I speak with them briefly. They leave for the cemetery while I head for school, taking the long way back so that I can pass by their house. I stop for a moment and observe the kitchen window. I imagine the inside of the house with Granny's rocking chair now empty. I begin to run. Memories of Granny flash through my mind like a parade of pictures as the snow crunches under my pounding feet. Stinging tears freeze in my eyes and then melt when I enter the school. I brush them away with my mitt. My classroom is silent because everyone is reading. I worm my way through the labyrinth of desks to my seat and open my text. The printed letters stare at me without rhyme or reason. After a moment of confusion, I run my fingers over the lines of print and their letters become words that register clearly in my mind, because Granny is somehow pointing me in the right direction. I can feel her presence, and embrace it as I eagerly read further.

We survive another winter on the farm. I haven't seen much of Dee and Lee because they are in "lo-o-o-ove" and going steady with some French guys. However, time passed quickly. Having the kids around made that possible. Mild weather promises the arrival of an early spring. I decide to convert the pantry downstairs into a bedroom for myself, because I want some privacy and the kids need more space upstairs. There is just enough room between the living room wall and my bed to walk to a cupboard where I store my clothes and prized possessions. The room has no windows, but I feel comfortable in the black velvet darkness. It reminds me of the jacket hanging on the hook at Aunt B's house. Every night, I watch my sister and her family pass by the foot of my bed as they make their way upstairs through my pantry bedroom. I wish them a goodnight and turn off the lamp when they disappear from view.

My dad is in the hospital after a hernia operation so Knight drives me in to visit him. He appears to be recuperating nicely and is overjoyed to see us. An old man in the bed next to Daddy's keeps interrupting our conversation. He reminds me of the old man with the beady eyes and gives me the creeps. I feel I shouldn't look at him, but my glance is briefly drawn to his eyes. I am overcome by the same feeling I experienced after the woman at the bazaar "oreeked" me. I quickly shift my eyes away but realize it is too late. By the time we return to the farm, I am nauseated. It is almost midnight so my sister and the kids are already asleep. I don't say anything to my brother-in-law who goes straight to bed. I pull my flannelette nightgown out of the pajama dog and slip it on. The sudden urge to vomit forces me to dash into the kitchen just in time to hoist the five-gallon slop pail out from under the sink. The pail is at least three-quarters full and foul smelling. I heave until my guts ache. Then I suddenly lose all of my energy as I struggle to lift the pail back into the cupboard. The bottom of the pail strikes the edge of the cupboard causing it to tilt and spill most of the slimy contents onto the floor. It spreads quickly soaking the bottom of my nightgown and making its way under the cookstove and over the floor. I grab floor rags and try to sop it up as quickly as I can to wring it back into the pail. The slow, smelly process causes me to gag repeatedly as I work. I don't allow myself to stop until I scrub the floor clean with a bucket of fresh soapy water. By then, I am sweating profusely. In desperation, I lick my hand, swipe it across my forehead, find an under section of the hem of my nightgown that isn't soaked with slop, and wipe my forehead with it. I yawn and spit to the side three times and repeat the procedure three times. I experience mixed feelings about what I am doing and can't imagine its helping, but I begin to regain my strength within minutes. After changing into pajamas, I rinse off the bottom of my nightgown leaving it in the pail and crawl into bed. I feel rejuvenated when I wake up in the morning even though I was emotionally and physically drained before falling asleep. I don't tell anybody about what happened. I don't want them to think that I am some kind of witch because I can receive the curse and use its cure.

When Daddy is released from the hospital, I am in town to meet him. I have changed the sheets on his bed and laundered a pair of pajamas left behind by one of our boarders—nothing like fresh sheets and pajamas to make a body feel better! Tears glisten in his eyes as he leans on me for support, and we slowly make our way to the bedroom. I watch him like a hawk for the next few days making sure he eats, rests, and exercises. By the time Mom comes home for Easter, he is up and around and back to his usual cheerful self.

The evening after Mom's return, I decide to walk over to Dee's house. I make it only as far as the egg station when a car loaded with kids from school pulls up beside me. The driver, who is in my class, asks me if I heard about my aunt's son being in a horrible accident. Apparently, he was electrocuted by a hot wire while working in a storm in the big city and is in critical condition. As the car pulls away, I turn around and walk back home in shock. When I tell Mom about the accident, the color drains from her face just as it did when she read the letter from Big Sis. Daddy is visibly shaken. I come to my senses and ask, "Should we go over there now? What if it isn't true?" We want to do the right thing and decide to wait until morning.

I toss and turn all night. My mother and I meet in the

kitchen after daybreak. We had both slept in our clothes and don't want anything for breakfast. I inform Daddy that we are leaving and then walk with Mom along Main Street in silence. I notice several cars parked in front of Aunt B's house, which is not a good sign. Mom taps gently on the door. It is unlocked so we enter when nobody answers. I look at the living room door directly in line with the kitchen door and think of Granny. The curtain is pushed to the side. My eyes move to the right, and I know he is dead when I see my aunt lying on the couch where her son recently slept. She has her arm bent over her face and is moaning quietly. Her older daughters are taking care of her, but she is oblivious to everything happening around her. I can hear the girls weeping out loud upstairs. Relatives, neighbors, and friends come and go. We sit there for a long time with each of us lost in our own thoughts. I feel so helpless and hopeless. I think about his chances of getting into heaven. They are pretty good, I conclude, according to Granny. He is a Christian man who pays his dues to the church. Could it be that the world really is controlled by an evil genius as Granny had often countered when she couldn't explain the horrors humans were forced to endure here on earth? The theory made sense. What would happen to us then? I don't have the answers.

Mom motions for me to leave with her as it is pointless to stay any longer. When I hesitate at the door, my eyes focus for a moment on the black velvet jacket hanging on its hook by the ladder. I quickly look away. Instead of blessing food for Easter, we attend the funeral, which is a heartbreaking experience. His wife is devastated and hardly able to walk. What will become of their son who is only a couple of months old? I am angry with God, who, in my mind, could never justify what happened to my cousin and his family.

53

On Easter Sunday, Smoky is lying outside by the back door. I'm sitting on the step beside him, watching him and thinking about Aunt B, her family, and the funeral. Whenever anyone walks by, he raises his head as he looks for attention. They seem compelled to pet him when they looked into his sad, irresistible eyes. Even Mom fusses over him, which is unusual. I speak to him for a moment, scratch him behind his ears, and give him a wave, just a little wave, before I go into the house. Later on that afternoon, I run outside to play with him. His body lies still, and I stretch out my hand to pet him. He doesn't respond and I know he is dead. Tears fall from my eyes onto his black fur. I know he couldn't live forever. Somehow, he must have sensed he was going to die and said his good-byes to everyone earlier in the day. Daddy throws him into the back of a truck, and the driver takes him away. Easter has never been a good time for our family.

Mom and Daddy are gone again, and I am back at the farm. I set up a high jump in the yard near the spruce trees. Running and landing on grass are not the best conditions for practicing but I keep at it for hours. Releasing energy helps me cope with my pent-up anger and frustration that built up over the Easter holiday.

The day before I turn fifteen, I wash my favorite sweater outside in a basin . It is a turquoise blue pullover that I want to wear for my birthday. I roll it in a towel to force out the excess moisture and hang it on the clothesline to dry while we spend the afternoon in town. When we return, I run to the line to retrieve my sweater and am shocked to find that most of the left sleeve is missing. I rip it off the line without removing the clothespins and stomp angrily into the house. I know who is guilty of this crime. It is one of the horses. I heard stories about their eating clothes off the line before. My sister gives me such a weird look when I hold up the sweater that I am forced to laugh, and she joins in. We laugh until we cry. It feels so good to laugh again. The next day she bakes a chocolate cake and decorates it with pink frosting and fifteen matching candles. After supper, when I blow them out, I realize how close we have grown. I have become part of their family. That feeling is a special birthday present to me. How could I ever repay them for letting me stay with them? I think about the baby killdeer before I fall asleep and feel guilty about not visiting its grave.

I win the high jump divisional and am looking forward to competing in the provincial meet in the big city. Two cars leave from our school. I ride with Eagle Beak and three other kids and am pestered by the sound of the wind whistling through the little side windows as we drive along. These days, I can't tolerate continuous noise, because it often leads to a migraine. The trip lasts for almost five hours because we stop for a snack. Everyone is anxious to get out of the car when we arrive at the grounds. After years of practicing, I find it strange and awkward jumping at the meet because we land on thick mats piled high, almost even with the bar. The winner is a girl who has successfully mastered the roll. I am tormented by the fact that my high jumping in competitions might very well be over. I don't have the coaching or facilities for even attempting the roll. Overall, I am pleased with my performance at the meet as I place fourth. I am also happy with my marks at school. They are high enough for me to be recommended in all subjects, which means I don't have to write final exams.

To celebrate the last day of school, most of the students from my class meet at the lake in the evening. We spend hours swimming and then build a huge bonfire. I am sitting on a log staring into it. When I look up, I notice someone watching me from the shadows. The figure comes closer. I feel an instant attraction to this person. His black hair shines blue, and his dark eyes glow in the firelight. He flashes a mysterious smile revealing perfect white teeth. Sitting down next to me, he says, "I saw pictures of you high jumping at the provincial meet. I've never seen anyone appear so focused. I coach speed skating in the city. From the determined look on your face, I decided that you would definitely be a perfect person to coach." I am surprised and flattered that he recognized me from the photos.

"Well, I don't think I'll be doing any more high jumping because emphasis at the meet was on perfecting the roll. I would need a coach, and we just don't have the equipment or the facilities for it. It wouldn't be fun landing on my back in a gravel pit," I remark with a chuckle. We continue with our conversation as if there is nobody else around. He is easy to talk to, has a great sense of humor, and repeatedly makes me laugh. He is probably the same age as Sunny. My eyes are again drawn to his black hair that glistens like coal in the firelight. At that moment, I decide to call him "Coal." Suddenly, someone douses the fire with a pail of water catapulting us back to reality. As we are surrounded by the black velvet night, we realize that the crowd is dispersing. I jump up abruptly and wave, just a little wave, as I run to catch a ride.

I hear him call, "See you," as I hop into the car. I am the first to be dropped off because I am staying in town. Only Daddy is home, and Mom will be back later in the week. A full moon has emerged from its cloud-cover. I feel so awake that I decide to visit the big rock. I've never been there at night before, and it's been so long since I've spoken with Johnny. I try to tell myself that it is because I don't need him any more, but the real reason is that I am avoiding him.

"I've missed you so much, Little Sister," says Johnny. I can tell by the tone of his voice that he means it.

"I just met this guy. He's the exact opposite of Sunny in looks. I can't stop thinking about him," I swoon with a sigh.

"You mean 'your Coal'?" teases Johnny in his know-it-all voice. "I can see you standing beside him as he places his arm around you. It's a bright winter's day. You are wearing a royal blue shaggy jacket, blue slacks, and the mukluks your dad bought you for Christmas. Your hair is in a ponytail held in place with the pearl clip. He is wearing a white toque and a deerskin jacket with fringes and embroidered with tiny colored beads. When he gazes into your eyes, you can't fathom how dark and deep his are. You are at his mercy and are drawn into them. His smile is no longer mysterious to you..."

"Johnny," I blurt out interrupting him. "Don't tell me anymore. I don't want to know how things turn out. I'm so tired I just want to go to bed," I mumble as I leave the rock and disappear into the shadows. I sneak into the house and down the hallway without waking my dad. As I lie in my bed in my Main Street Bedroom, I think about Sunny and Coal and how different and, yet, how alike they are.

54

School is out for the summer. A boy who lives across the street from Granny's house has a crush on me and follows me every where I go. He is short and stocky with brown hair that falls flat against his head and wears pop-bottle glasses. One afternoon, when I am sitting in the living room watching an old movie, I am disturbed by a tap on the picture window. I glance up and identify the culprit as that boy, who runs off thinking I didn't see him. I consider him harmless so I again devote my attention to the movie.

Within a few minutes, there is a thud at the window. I assume it is that boy again; but when I look out, I spot a dead sparrow on the sill. As I bury it by the garden, my thoughts are overshadowed by the superstitious belief that if a bird hits a window somebody will die within three days. I try to brush my uneasiness aside, but it won't go away. Three days later, I decide to do the laundry. Several loads of Daddy's work clothes litter the kitchen floor by the washer. When the tub is full of whites that I ran through the wringer, I carry it outside to the clothesline. It is a hot, sunny day with a bit of a breeze and perfect for drying. I proceed to pin a T-shirt on the line when a sudden, deafening explosion makes the ground shake and lifts me off my feet. My heart begins to pound because I know something terrible has happened. I run around the side of the house in the direction of where the explosion originated and look toward the garage across the street. Daddy is already there. Men are frantically scurrying about trying to gain control of the situation. I run past the egg station. A semi is parked beside it and that boy is lying on the ground. Part of his skull is missing and its remains, including his eyeball, are splattered on the egg station wall. His body is twitching. I move forward to help, but one of the men hollers, "Don't come here! Get back!" I comply with my legs becoming limp. A car that is being filled with gas at the pump suddenly backs up. Two men lift the body, place it in the back seat, and cover it with a blanket. The car speeds off with gravel flying in all directions. Fortunately for me, a truck pulls up and the driver asks me what happened, which brings me to my senses because I am forced to answer.

"I think someone is dead," I stammer. That boy did die as a result of the freakish accident. He had apparently hit the rim of one of the truck tires with a hammer. The rim, which was under great pressure, somehow disengaged from the tire and flew up hitting his head and killing him instantly. I attend his funeral, which is a sad event. I am sorry for his parents because he was their only son, and I am angry because he was too young to die. According to Granny, he will have no problem getting into heaven, as if that were any consolation. Again, I question the existence of a loving God. I cannot stop thinking about that boy tapping on the window and the bird hitting the very same spot three days prior to the accident. Was it all just a coincidence? It just couldn't be, but what could it mean?

A couple of days later, after our lives have returned to normal, Mom comes home. Daddy and I always keep the house tidy. As soon as Mom is there, the place can only be described as being "upside-down." He laughs when he surveys the mess on the cupboard counters and comments, "You can sure tell when Mom is home." Her problem was that she never put anything away after she used it. I have a full-time job cleaning up after her while she is busy baking and cooking. Whenever she washes clothes, I must finish the task, which means running them through the wringer and hanging them on the clothesline. Then I have to take them off, fold or iron them, and put them away. Every time she brings home groceries, she just sets the bags on the cupboard and table, leaving it up to me to put things away.

After Mom and Daddy leave, I spend a couple of weeks with Med Sis helping her around the house and baby-sitting. Then I am back in my pantry bedroom on the farm. I haven't missed a dance or wedding all summer and enjoy myself the most when Sunny is playing. I am happy to be back in school in my crowded Grade IX and X room. We have the same teachers, except for a new history teacher, who has taken on that subject for the principal in order to ease the latter's workload. After a couple of weeks, he must have noticed my interest in the learning because, one day, after class, he asks me what my plans are after completing high school. "You're university material," he comments nodding his head in a positive manner.

I smile thinking that Johnny predicted I would one day get a degree and answer, "I've been thinking about going to university. Thanks for your confidence in me." As I walk home from school, I know I shouldn't get my hopes up too high. There is the problem of a lack of money, but I could work my way through. Then there is the problem of getting to the big city. If I took a bus there, where would I stay? I decide not to worry about it. Besides, the most important thing for me to do right now is to finish high school. One thing I do have in my favor is the box of notebooks in the closet upstairs. If I write small enough and don't waste any space, they will surely last me until I complete Grade XII.

55

One chilly morning in early October, I awaken to the sound
of chickens squawking. I dress quickly and dash out the
door in time to see my brother-in-law chopping the head off
a white hen. It escapes and hops around the yard with its
neck sticking out of its breast and blood spattering in all
directions before falling to the ground and giving its last few
twitches. Small Sis is standing at a tub secured over a fire on
a metal framework where she is dunking chickens into
boiling water to facilitate the plucking of feathers. Several
naked hens with their insides removed are already lying in a
pile beside her. I intended to help but cannot tolerate the
nauseating smell of the wet feathers and guts. Knight calls
me over daring me to behead a chicken he has on the block.
I grab the hen by its stiff legs as he hands me the ax. In sheer
desperation, I fight to align its neck with the parallel
grooves in the wood as it keeps twisting its head. Then the
hen manages to turn enough to look at me with frightened
red eyes and begins to cry like a baby. I can't kill it and
proceed to release the bird, which thankfully flutters away
to safety. As I run to the house in the opposite direction,
Daddy's words echo in my brain yet again, "Let live," with a
long "i" as in "alive."

The days following the chicken incident seem to pass
ever so slowly. I can hardly wait for the Halloween dance,
the most popular annual event held at the Finn Hall, a mile
down the road from the farm. An added bonus is that

Sunny's band will be playing. Finally, the night I am waiting for arrives. I decide to dress up like a man so that I can enjoy the privilege of asking girls to dance with me. I have stashed an assortment of my brother-in-law's clothes in my room for my costume. After donning his black and red checkered shirt and striped overalls, I ask my sister help me stuff them with thin pillows. His cap, which I secure on my head over my flattened ponytail, compliments the rubbery mask with bushy eyebrows and mustache just perfectly. I complete the disguise with work gloves to hide my painted fingernails and three pairs of socks to keep his boots from slipping off my feet. When I look into the mirror, I agree with the whole family that nobody could ever guess who I was. In fact, the kids are somewhat afraid of me.

Knight gives me a ride and lets me out before reaching the hall's driveway to ensure that nobody sees me leave his truck. He agrees to pick me up in an hour and a half so that I can change out of my costume. As I walk toward the hall, I savor the sweet sound of Sunny's fiddle music, which drifts into the darkness from the open windows. I pay for a ticket and survey the room from the doorway. Very few people are wearing costumes. Sunny is up on the stage with his fiddle tucked under his chin, his bow and fingers flying, and his foot stomping. He doesn't smile at me this time— instead, he laughs, and I realize he'd know me no matter what I was wearing. When his band switches into its rock 'n roll mode, I motion for one of the girls to join me on the floor. She doesn't want to dance with me at first, but her friends dare her to. I begin to jive twirling her around and catching her off guard in a positive way. "You're a good dancer," she comments in a surprised voice. The guys standing around by the door try to guess my identity but aren't even quite sure that I am not a man. Time passes quickly as I dance with most of the girls. Then I sneak out in the middle of a polka and meet Knight where he dropped me off.

Back at the farm, I quickly change into the turquoise, brown, and white checkered linen dress that I ordered from the catalogue. The top is tight fitting with short sleeves, and the skirt has narrow pleats running from the waist to just below the knee. A slightly draped golden chain attached to the right of the buckle decorates the belt that is covered with the same fabric as the dress. I quickly and expertly style my hair into a French twist with the three bobby pins and slip on the brown shoes, which are now my favorite for dancing. I remember to dab on some Chanel No. 5 before I run out the door. Knight drives me back to the dance as planned. Ticket sales are over because it is getting late. One of the guys asks me to dance as soon as I step into the hall. There is Sunny smiling at me again. The hall is so small I feel I am always in his sight, and I know he is following my every move with his eyes. Dee and her boyfriend arrive late, as usual, and badger me into going out to his car for a while because one of the guys from school wants to talk to me. I am enjoying Sunny's music so much that I just want to dance, dance, and dance. They keep after me until I, finally, give in to them. When we get into the car, of course, their plan is to take a short drive. Precious minutes tick away, and I realize there is no point in going back to the dance because it will soon be over. They are heading for the lake, but I insist that they take me back to the farm. I get my way. I am pretty disappointed when one of the girls at school tells me that Sunny waited for me to come back to the dance because he wanted to take me home.

56

During the second week of November, the kids get sick. We had heard of several cases of scarlet fever in the area, but my sister is convinced they have measles. Their symptoms include a high temperature and a fine red rash that covers the entire body. She keeps them in bed, and we take turns sponging them off to keep the fever under control. Their condition improves after several days, and the rash disappears. Some time later, I develop a sore throat. The pain is so severe that I go to inspect my mouth in the mirror and notice a strange bright red blotch under both of my eyes. I had never before seen anything like it. I am very tired and decide I was lucky to have contracted the flu on the weekend because I can sleep in and be ready for school on Monday. When I awaken in the middle of the night, I know I am running a high temperature. I can barely sit up but turn on my lamp and force myself to get a face cloth and basinful of lukewarm water that I set on the stool beside my bed. As I sponge off my arms and neck, I notice the familiar red rash that now covers my body. I place the damp face cloth on my forehead for a moment and repeat the process of sponging off my body and face until I fall asleep.

I am extremely ill for the next couple of days, to the point of being delirious, and drink as much water as possible because I feel I need it in order to survive. Since my eyes are sensitive to light, the most comfortable place for me is in my pantry bedroom. Instead of being back in school on

Monday, I am absent from several days of classes. I am concerned about not being able to catch up with all of the work I missed. I tell my sister to write a note to my principal, explaining that I have the flu, and to send me my homework with a neighbor. When I receive the assignments, I am too sick to look at them and don't seem to care. I lose interest in everything around me and grow weaker, hour by hour. The only thing I am able to eat is the occasional slice of banana because my throat burns so badly. Eventually, my throat becomes so tender I can eat nothing; and even swallowing water becomes impossible.

My brother-in-law returns from the fish camp to pick up supplies that are to arrive by bus in the hospital town late at night. I tell him that I want him to take me along and drop me off at the hospital. When the time comes for us to leave, I bundle myself up. I have been in the house for so long that the frigid air, which immediately envelopes me as I step out the door, feels so good. My sister's worried face appears in the frosted kitchen window, and she watches me as I climb into the truck. We drive in silence. I can't speak because my throat is so sore. I know that nuns run the hospital and fear they won't believe how sick I am. When we arrive at the hospital and park, I ask my brother-in-law to come in with me, but he refuses. I hesitate, having second thoughts about walking in by myself. The lights in the hospital windows glow ominously, as if taunting me to come in. I realize that Knight won't take me in because, if I do enter that building, I will die there.

I can't explain it, but I begin to feel better—a sensation, which seems to creep over me like a blanket being pulled up slowly from my feet to my head. I tell Knight that I don't want to go in because I am feeling better. He nods his head, starts up the truck, and drives to the bus depot to pick up the supplies. I must have fallen asleep, because I can't remember the trip home. As I crawl into bed, I face the fact that I am not better. I shiver all night in a half-asleep state.

The next morning, I am inundated with a hopeless, helpless feeling. I can taste death. As the day progresses, it begins to storm. My brother-in-law decides not to return to the fish camp. I listen to the wind howling in the chimney above my head. It's like a trumpet heralding me on my final journey. Even at her young age, Princess Blue Eyes is concerned about me. She creeps into my pantry bedroom and sits on the edge of my bed. She has learned a new word, "remember". She keeps repeating it over and over again. Then, every one of her sentences begins with the word. I don't know when she leaves, but I do begin to remember. I remember the good times I had with Daddy, Mom, Granny, and the Frenchies. I remember Johnny's prophecies. I remember Big Sis, Med Sis, Small Sis, the Czars, the Dukes, the Knights, and the Princesses. I remember the dresses Mom sewed for me and the beautiful bridesmaids' gowns. I remember Smoky, Tubby, Nancy, and Fluffy. I remember Pumpkinhead, the reindeer with its eyes frozen open, and the baby killdeer. I remember high jumping, running, riding my bike, and answering questions in school. I remember Sunny and Coal. I remember the troll, who now symbolizes the negative forces in my life. I remember Old Man Click. I remember Granny's stories and our discussions about heaven and hell.

My remembering is interrupted when Small Sis, Knight, and the kids pass through the far end of my room in single file to quietly climb the stairs as they go to bed early. I watch them sensing that I will never see them again. Small Sis whispers, "Good night." I wave, just a little wave, and turn out my light as they disappear up the stairs. I sink back onto my pillows. I wonder what Mom and Daddy will say when they find out I'm dead. I don't care. I hear Daddy's words,

"Die, die once. Happy, the day you born. Happy, the day you die." I am slipping away and am prepared for whatever lies ahead, but I really don't want to go to heaven. I don't want to see people running around in white dresses or listen to their music. I don't want to reunite with loved ones, not even with Granny. The magic we once had on earth could never again be recaptured. I know what I do want. I want it to be the way it was before I was born, with nothing there. I feel myself being drawn into black velvet. It's so warm and so welcoming… I allow myself to fall, down, down, down… Then distant voices disturb me and lure me unwillingly from my blissful abyss of darkness.

"Are they voices of angels?" I ask myself in a stupor. "I hope they aren't the voices of Peter and Paul. I don't want to enter the kind of world I left behind." My eyes flutter open and I can see where I am… I'm in my pantry bedroom… I'm so disappointed that I'm still in my bed that I want to scream. I wanted to die and I was prepared to die. I think I did, but I came back. I feel cheated. Someday, again, I will have to face and accept death. It isn't fair…. I thought Johnny lied to me, but now I realize that there is a strong possibility that all of the prophecies he made will come true. I have returned from peaceful darkness to unwanted reality. Then I focus on the muffled voices, which, I realize, are originating in the kitchen.

Then Small Sis tiptoes into my room and whispers, "There's a strange man in the kitchen. I don't know how he got here. It's so stormy outside. He must have walked because I think our road is blocked. I told him that my husband is doing chores and should be back soon. I also told him that my sister is very ill. Look at these pills. He assures me that you will get better if you take them because they contain penicillin. For some reason, I can sense that he knows you; but I've never seen him before. I made him coffee and toast, but he hasn't touched it." I examine the tablets that are stacked in a metal cylinder. "I'm going back to the kitchen because the kids are alone with him. Come and have a look at him," she urges as she disappears into the living room.

I force myself to sit up and push my legs over the edge of the bed with my hands. My nightie is twisted around my body. I am very weak but manage to get out of bed, slide my feet into my slippers, and slowly make my way out of my pantry bedroom. I can't believe I didn't hear my sister and the kids pass through my room. I must have been dead—be it for seconds, minutes, or hours. My knees begin to buckle so I grab onto the living room doorway to steady myself. The light in the kitchen is too bright. For a moment, my eyes cannot focus; but then I see the man. I can see him clearly. He is a man of small stature, dressed in a gray jacket and pants. The grayness of his long hair matches the salt-and-pepper stubble on his narrow face. When we make eye contact he stands up and moves toward the kitchen door. He holds me with the ice-blue eyes, which, I know, have the power to view the depths of my being, and throws me a captivating smile. Then he speaks in an all-too-familiar voice saying, "Take the pills you have in your hand. They will make you well. I must go, now that I know you will be okay." He opens the door as I run after him. My brain isn't functioning properly, leaving me momentarily confused. However, the pieces of the puzzle fall into place when I pinpoint the identity of the man with the voice. Yes! I know who he is. Swirling snow greets me as I open the door wide. I begin to panic when I can't see him.

I summon all of my remaining strength and manage to call, "Don't go, Johnny! Don't go, Johnny! Don't go!" Before my very eyes, the swirling snow changes to dust caught up in a whirlwind, which I observe from underneath it as I lie in the hollow of my rock. I realize that I have been lying here for a long time, but I don't want to move. I am surrounded by Johnny's presence. I raise my head. "Johnny," I call. "It's me." There is no answer. "The medicine worked. I did get better," I continue in a small voice trying to assure myself that he will answer, but all that I hear is the wind. I must face the fact that Johnny is gone now just like my house and my rock. He is gone now just like Granny, Mom, and Daddy. My thoughts return to having to face death again someday. I experience an urgent desire to visit my daddy's grave as my mind is bombarded with pertinent questions, what will become of me when I die? will I be buried in Mom's cemetery? or, will I be buried in the cemetery on the other side of town next to Daddy's grave?

The solution becomes clear to me. It would, of course, be best for my body to be cremated and have my ashes scattered somewhere in between—on the road in front of the Main Street Bedroom, which still exists in my mind, or here in the hollow of my rock. I could rest peacefully in either of these familiar surroundings because I would be at home where I belong. My thoughts move on to other unresolved issues. I never before realized how much religion and death have shaped my childhood. I am tired of both of them. From now on, instead of religion, I choose common sense. Instead of death, I choose life. Johnny wanted me to live, and I know in my heart that he saved me from the clutches of scarlet fever. I hear Daddy's words in his dear voice, "Let live," with a long "i" as in "alive." His words instill in me the incentive and desire to live to be as old as Granny and to gather wisdom along the way as she did. As I follow in Granny's footsteps, I hope I am blessed, definitely not in the religious sense, with a little girl who wants me to read to her.

I lie back in the hollow that cradles me like a baby, not wanting to leave, and try to hold onto home for a moment longer.

Bible and Dictionary References

The Holy Bible, New International Version. Seven Oaks, Kent: Hodder and Stoughton Ltd., Mill Road, Dunton Green, 1980.

Webster's New Twentieth Century Dictionary of the English Language, Unabridged, Second Edition. Cleveland and New York: The World Publishing Company, 1960.